COLLIER
OF WALES

ENGINEERING & ARCHITECTURE

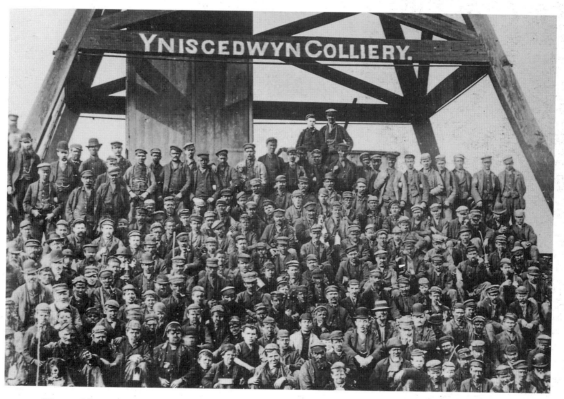

The workforce at 'Yniscedwyn Colliery', Swansea Valley, in the early twentieth century. (T.J.Davies)

Royal Commission on the Ancient and Historical Monuments of Wales

COLLIERIES OF WALES

ENGINEERING & ARCHITECTURE

Stephen Hughes

Stephen Hughes, Brian Malaws, Medwyn Parry & Peter Wakelin

for *the*

Royal Commission on the Ancient and Historical Monuments of Wales

ISBN 1-871184-11-8

British Library Cataloguing in Publication Data. A catalogue record for this book is available from the British Library.

Printed in Wales by
Mid Wales Litho Limited,
Units 12 &13, Pontyfelin Industrial Estate, New Inn, Pontypool, Gwent, NP4 OGD
Telephone - 0495 750033   Fax - 0495 751466

Cover: The headframe at Merthyr Vale Colliery, one of John Nixon's designs with banded bull-head rail supports.
Back Cover: The Engine Pit Level of ca.1810, that still survives below the Big Pit Colliery Museum at Blaenavon.

Royal Commission on the Ancient and Historical Monuments of Wales
Plas Crug, Aberystwyth, Dyfed, SY23 1NJ
Telephone - 01972 621233   Fax - 01972 627701
The Royal Commission was established in 1908 to make an inventory of the ancient and historical monuments of Wales and Monmouthshire. It is currently empowered by a Royal Warrant of 1992 to survey, record, publish and maintain a database of ancient, historical and maritime sites and structures, and landscapes in Wales. It is responsible for the National Monuments Record of Wales which is open daily for public reference, for the supply of archaeological information to the Ordnance Survey for mapping purposes, for the co-ordination of archaeological aerial photography in Wales, and for the sponsorship of the regional Sites and Monuments Records.

Chairman :
    Professor J. B.Smith, M.A., F.R.Hist.S.
Commissioners :
    Professor R.W.Brunskill, O.B.E., Ph.D., F.S.A.
    Professor D.Ellis Evans, D.Phil., F.B.A.
    Professor R.A.Griffiths, Ph.D., D.Litt., F.R.Hist.S
    D.Gruffydd Jones, B.A., F.R.S.A.
    R.M.Haslam, M.A., F.S.A.
    Professor G.D.B.Jones, D.Phil., F.S.A.
    Mrs. A.Nicol, M.A., B.Litt., F.R.Hist.S.
    S.B.Smith, M.Sc., F.M.A., F.R.S.A.
    Professor G.J.Wainwright, M.B.E., Ph.D., F.S.A.
    E.Wiliam, Ph.D., F.S.A.
Secretary :
    P.R.White, B.A., F.S.A.

AUTHORSHIP AND ACKNOWLEDGEMENTS

The layout and design of this volume has been carried out by John Johnston, and drawings have been prepared by Charles Green and Medwyn Parry. Modern ground photography is by Iain Wright and aerial photography by Chris Musson; underground photography is largely from the John Cornwell Collection in the National Monuments Record of Wales. Thanks are due to the management, Inspectorate and staff of Cadw: Welsh Historic Monuments for their time and assistance given. The text has been much improved with the advice of Brian Davies of Pontypridd Heritage Centre, Michael Tutton (formerly of British Coal) and Professor Ronald Brunskill, Professor Ralph Griffiths and Stuart Smith. Richard Suggett has acted as copy-editor. The officers of British Coal have been of much help in arranging access to sites and in the location of surviving drawings. The Welsh Development Agency also helped facilitate work. Jacqueline Rose of the Public Record Office has been of particular assistance in arranging for the transfer of valuable British Coal Records to the National Monuments Record of Wales and other public archives. The Parliamentary Select Committee for Welsh Affairs has also shown interest in seeing that the remaining colliery drawings are safeguarded. The assistance of the South Wales Institute of Engineers has been much valued.

Contents

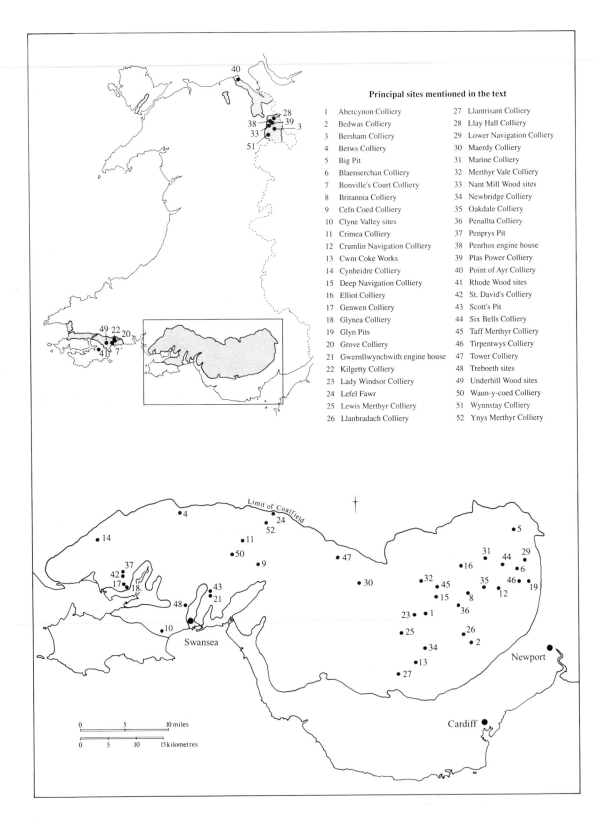

Principal sites mentioned in the text

1	Abercynon Colliery	27	Llantrisant Colliery
2	Bedwas Colliery	28	Llay Hall Colliery
3	Bersham Colliery	29	Lower Navigation Colliery
4	Betws Colliery	30	Maerdy Colliery
5	Big Pit	31	Marine Colliery
6	Blaenserchan Colliery	32	Merthyr Vale Colliery
7	Bonville's Court Colliery	33	Nant Mill Wood sites
8	Britannia Colliery	34	Newbridge Colliery
9	Cefn Coed Colliery	35	Oakdale Colliery
10	Clyne Valley sites	36	Penallta Colliery
11	Crimea Colliery	37	Penprys Pit
12	Crumlin Navigation Colliery	38	Penrhos engine house
13	Cwm Coke Works	39	Plas Power Colliery
14	Cynheidre Colliery	40	Point of Ayr Colliery
15	Deep Navigation Colliery	41	Rhode Wood sites
16	Elliot Colliery	42	St. David's Colliery
17	Genwen Colliery	43	Scott's Pit
18	Glynea Colliery	44	Six Bells Colliery
19	Glyn Pits	45	Taff Merthyr Colliery
20	Grove Colliery	46	Tirpentwys Colliery
21	Gwernllwynchwith engine house	47	Tower Colliery
22	Kilgetty Colliery	48	Treboeth sites
23	Lady Windsor Colliery	49	Underhill Wood sites
24	Lefel Fawr	50	Waun-y-coed Colliery
25	Lewis Merthyr Colliery	51	Wynnstay Colliery
26	Llanbradach Colliery	52	Ynys Merthyr Colliery

Preface

From about the time of the 1984-85 miners' strike it became obvious that the coal industry was in a period of rapid contraction. However the accelerated decline of the Industry led the Royal Commission, through its liaison forum of the *Welsh Industrial Archaeology Panel*, to seek advice on what the immediate recording priorities should be. Subsequently the Royal Commission instituted a programme of work in the complementary areas of field recording and the safeguarding of original architectural and engineering drawings. This publication is intended to illustrate the campaign of work.

In the field the initial task was to photograph the collieries still operating, paying special attention to the installations highlighted as being of particular interest. At the same time Royal Commission staff attempted to establish what drawings already existed, and what gaps needed to be filled by new measured surveys of important installations. Alongside this work on the ground, the Royal Commission's aerial photographer was active in recording the large colliery complexes from the air. This allowed complete complexes to be clearly pictured in their context of transport, topography, settlements and spoil tips.

Two large sets of original Edwardian colliery design drawings were located at the technical headquarters of British Coal in Bretby, Derbyshire, and have been indexed at the Royal Commission, prior to being transferred to the Glamorgan Archives Service. Most other early colliery design drawings had disappeared before. However, British Coal and the Public Record Office helped facilitate the transfer of many thousands of microfilm copies of later engineering drawings of Bersham Colliery and many south Wales pits to the Royal Commission's *National Monuments Record of Wales*. Subsequently a similar exercise took place in England. Also at Bretby had been the extensive collection of design drawings from the Tredomen Engineering Works. Built to service the extensive Powell Duffryn Collieries, these Works had continued to supply British Coal until their closure in the latter 1980s. These drawings are now in safe storage at the National Library of Wales. Many architectural drawings of colliery baths and miners' houses were also transferred from British Coal to the Royal Commission and have now been rehoused in Gwent Record Office at Cwmbrân.

A freelance photographer, John Cornwell, had amassed an invaluable archive recording Welsh coalmines underground. A substantial part of this collection was purchased from Mr. Cornwell and is available for public consultation alongside the other survey results in the Royal Commission's *National Monuments Record of Wales*. This complements British Coal's own photographic record of the south Wales pits; some, which had been copied from the former Group Headquarters at Tredomen are reproduced here.

The purpose of this publication is to portray the main surface elements of working Welsh collieries as they survived into the 1980s and 1990s - almost invariably multi-period complexes with structures adapted and re-adapted during successive rebuildings and enlargements. This book seeks to portray in simple terms the technology used in relation to these structures and buildings; and also to place them in a historical context. It is hoped that others will be encouraged to explore in greater depth the archives which have been safeguarded and to interpret further the 'archaeology' of what was one of the most significant industries in the formation of modern Wales.

The classic large colliery of the later nineteenth century was dominated by tall engine-houses, as here at Deep Navigation Colliery, with one tall winding-house to the left and the pumping engine-house to the right. In 1872-79, at the time of sinking, the colliery, at 2,280 ft. (695 m.), was the deepest in south Wales. The hipped building to the right enclosed a huge 100 in. (2.54 m.) diameter cylinder high-pressure Cornish pumping-engine from the Perran Foundry, with an 11 ft. (3.35 m.) stroke lifting 350 gallons per minute. The large engine-house to the left held an inverted vertical 7 ft. (2.13 m.) stroke steam-engine by Fowler of Leeds, with the 54 in. (1.37 m.) cylinder supported over the top of the 32 ft. (9.75 m.) diameter winding-drum. During electrification in 1921-25 the tall beam-engine house was demolished and replaced by smaller electric pumps. The two winding-houses were only demolished down to their plinths as they provided the firm foundations for the elegant backstays of the large wrought-iron headframes with 20 ft. (6.1 m.) diameter winding sheaves (pulleys) supported 81 ft. 6 in. (24.84 m.) above the top of the shaft. At the time of closure of the pit in spring 1991 one wrought-iron headframe remained in use with an original steam-winch still enclosed within the foundations of the winding-engine house (as also at Marine Colliery); on the rear of the original engine-house plinth illustrated sat the stone-built electric winder engine-house of 1921 until demolition of the pit commenced in June 1991.

Introduction

The coal industry of south and north-eastern Wales first reached truly large proportions in the late eighteenth and early nineteenth centuries feeding the fuel-hungry iron and copper industries. However, by the mid-nineteenth century the great steam-coal trade of south Wales was beginning to dwarf even this. Coal exported principally from Cardiff was fuelling huge international steamship fleets and the Cardiff Coal Exchange determined the world price for such coal. Production in the south Wales coalfield peaked in 1913, at which time it had one of the largest outputs of any coalfield in the world. It remained the largest coalfield in Britain from then until 1925. North-eastern Wales had a smaller though still substantial coal industry.

The survival rate of the large intricate functional structures of the coal industry has not been good. Many structures could not be turned easily to new uses, and some, like headframes, were delicate forms, and unlike the masonry blast-furnaces of the earlier iron industry, which survive in large numbers, were easy to demolish. Combined with the demand for renewal and reclamation of sites, this factor meant that few examples, even of quite recent collieries, survive today.

The Welsh coal industry has been of outstanding importance throughout the past three hundred years. Well over 2,000 collieries are thought to have operated in the old counties of Pembrokeshire, Carmarthenshire, Breconshire, Glamorgan, Monmouthshire, Flintshire, Denbighshire and Anglesey. The industry was at the heart of the industrial revolution in Wales, participating in the development of new methods and technologies which were of world importance. Coalmining has been a significant activity both in its own right and for its integral role in other key Welsh industries. As the economic foundation of many communities, towns and cities during the past three hundred years, it has had a fundamental impact on the history and landscape of Wales.

At its peak in the early twentieth century, the south Wales coalfield had the largest export of any in the world, and dominated coal markets as far apart as the Mediterranean, South America, Africa and the Far East[1]. The ports of Cardiff and Barry became the leading ports 'by tonnage handled' anywhere in the world, and nearly all of their trade was in coal.

During the industrial revolution, and especially in the late eighteenth and early nineteenth centuries, the Welsh coal industry was at the forefront of the development of new techniques, structures, and modes of organization in mining. In Wales important advances were made, for example, in the development of horse-drawn railways and later steam railways, the use of water power for winding, the development of mine ventilation, the evolution of steam-engines for winding and pumping, the use of canals and tramroads for underground transport, and the evolution of mining communities and businesses. Welsh miners and Welsh mining companies took their skills and their capital to many parts of the world to develop other coalfields, from Russia to Pennsylvania. The all-important transfer from wood to coal as a fuel in the industrial revolution, and the increasing sophistication in the exploitation of coal, was heavily influenced by Welsh practices. These were developed by many early iron, tinplate and non-ferrous works which owned and ran their own collieries and which are notable names in industrial history: Cyfarthfa, Bersham, Dowlais, Aberdulais, Llangyfelach, and Ynysgedwyn.

Coalmining was a mainstay of the Welsh economy from the eighteenth century onwards, both as a direct wealth creator and as the supplier of fuel to other industries. At its peak around 1914 coalmining in Wales employed a quarter of a million people: one in four adult males in the country as a whole, and three in four in the Valleys. The demand created by the coal industry was the foundation of the transport industry of Wales, especially its dense railway network and its shipping industry, the Welsh commercial sector, and the engineering industry. Coal fuelled most of the other important Welsh industries of the eighteenth to mid-twentieth centuries, notably the iron and steel industries, tinplate, non-ferrous metals, brickmaking and pottery. The steam-coals produced in Wales fuelled steam boilers in locomotives, ships and factories within the country and outside.

The coal industry was the prime force in creating

the landscapes and communities which still characterize the Valleys, and was the chief impetus to industrial regions in north Wales and to the growth of urban centres along the coast, including Cardiff and Swansea. Many people regard mining as having had a central influence in Welsh communities and culture since the nineteenth century. The dangers and difficult labour relations of mining created close communities and influenced political development, education, literature and a host of other facets of Welsh nationhood.

Coal has been used in Wales since at least Roman times[2] and quarrying at exposed outcrops is documented from the thirteenth century. It was mined at first on a small scale for local use, but a long-distance trade in coal by sea developed during the seventeenth and eighteenth centuries, especially in Pembrokeshire and the areas around Llanelli and Swansea Bay. Mining at this time was primitive, starting with opencasts on exposed seams and bell-pits, and multiple shallow pits with short galleries, but developed with the use of tunnels driven into hillsides ('levels') and the use of wooden-tracked railways.

Development accelerated in the second half of the eighteenth century with the application of coal to smelting iron, copper, zinc and lead. These industries were focused mainly around Neath and Swansea, Llanelli, the Denbighshire coalfield, and the Heads of the Valleys region. Mining became much more highly capitalized, both for sea sale and industrial use. Wooden waggonways were extended over greater distances, steam-engines were introduced for pumping, ventilation furnaces were introduced, and relatively deep shafts were sunk, some using prototype steam winding-engines.

A further boost to expansion and capitalisation came at the end of the eighteenth century as the construction of canals led to the expansion of mining in inland areas which could look to external markets for the first time. Expansion was further assisted by the continued and phenomenal growth of the smelting industries in both north and south Wales, but especially in the south, where the Swansea region and the Heads of the Valleys region respectively became the dominant world centres for the production of copper and iron. Expansion brought with it the first iron railways, underground canals, organized mining complexes with steam power applied systematically, and mining in much deeper shafts. The use of water power was also developed to a fine art, powering both winding and pumping at many sites.

The introduction of steam railways together with the exploration of the steam-coal area of the central south Wales coalfield between about 1840 and the First World War brought phenomenal expansion. At the end of this period, the Welsh coal trade reached a peak of output and employment at which 620 mines were in operation in south Wales alone. Deep mines had been sunk in the centre of the coalfield and new urban communities grew up throughout the Valleys to supply labour. Steam power began to be used on a majestic scale, and underground haulage by steam-engine or compressed air became common. Coal-preparation plants to screen and wash the coal were in widespread use and mechanical ventilation by fan was pioneered, with great implications for safety and output.

Decline in the Welsh coalfields began around the time of the First World War and accelerated throughout the middle and late twentieth century. Many new mines were sunk, particularly in the concealed western part of the south Wales coalfield; but there was a steep aggregate decline in numbers of mines and miners. Technology continued to improve, with underground and surface conveyors, coal-preparation plants becoming more widespread, and the general use of electricity for surface machinery and underground for power and lighting, supplied by on-site power stations or later the National Grid. Welfare improved, with colliery baths and medical centres becoming more widespread, then ubiquitous after nationalization in 1947, and rescue centres established in central locations. By 1981 the number of mines had declined to 35, apart from small licensed operations and a growing number of opencast projects. This has fallen again so that only three large collieries are active in Wales in 1994.

References

1   H. Stanley Jevons, *The British Coal Trade* (London, 1915; reprinted, Newton Abbot, 1969), pp.678-81.
2   H. James, *Excavations in Roman Carmarthen, 1978-90* (forthcoming).

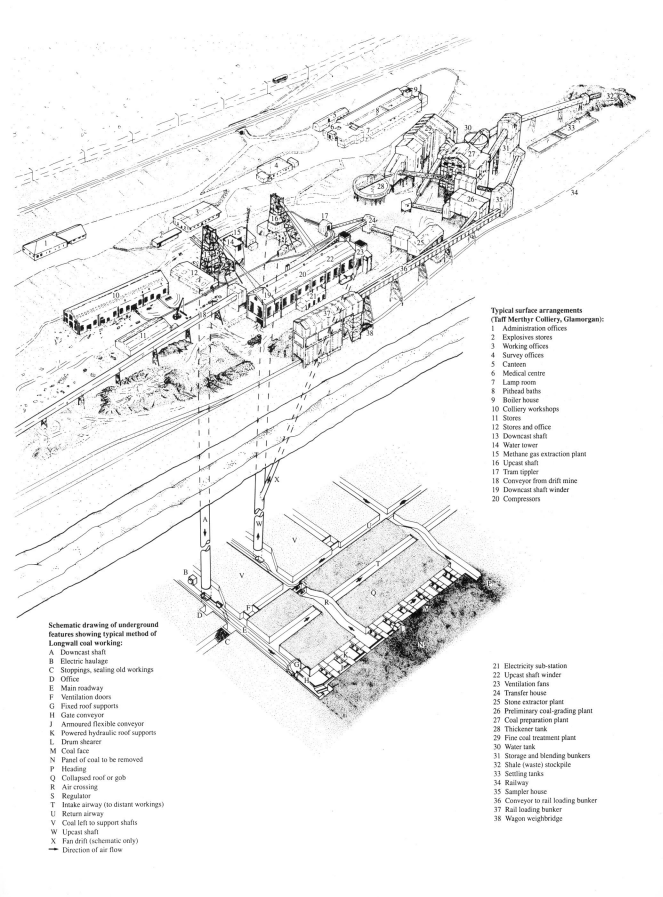

**Typical surface arrangements
(Taff Merthyr Colliery, Glamorgan):**

1   Administration offices
2   Explosives stores
3   Working offices
4   Survey offices
5   Canteen
6   Medical centre
7   Lamp room
8   Pithead baths
9   Boiler house
10 Colliery workshops
11 Stores
12 Stores and office
13 Downcast shaft
14 Water tower
15 Methane gas extraction plant
16 Upcast shaft
17 Tram tippler
18 Conveyor from drift mine
19 Downcast shaft winder
20 Compressors

21 Electricity sub-station
22 Upcast shaft winder
23 Ventilation fans
24 Transfer house
25 Stone extractor plant
26 Preliminary coal-grading plant
27 Coal preparation plant
28 Thickener tank
29 Fine coal treatment plant
30 Water tank
31 Storage and blending bunkers
32 Shale (waste) stockpile
33 Settling tanks
34 Railway
35 Sampler house
36 Conveyor to rail loading bunker
37 Rail loading bunker
38 Wagon weighbridge

**Schematic drawing of underground
features showing typical method of
Longwall coal working:**

A   Downcast shaft
B   Electric haulage
C   Stoppings, sealing old workings
D   Office
E   Main roadway
F   Ventilation doors
G   Fixed roof supports
H   Gate conveyor
J   Armoured flexible conveyor
K   Powered hydraulic roof supports
L   Drum shearer
M   Coal face
N   Panel of coal to be removed
P   Heading
Q   Collapsed roof or gob
R   Air crossing
S   Regulator
T   Intake airway (to distant workings)
U   Return airway
V   Coal left to support shafts
W   Upcast shaft
X   Fan drift (schematic only)
→   Direction of air flow

The Planning and Design of Collieries

Many surface layouts at collieries seem to have evolved by a process of amorphous growth and adaptation. Prior to the late nineteenth century the opportunities to build grand organized colliery layouts in advance of generating profits seem to have been limited. The multiple and divided ownership of the old-established British coalfields militated against the large-scale planning that characterized the development of many of the new coalfields of continental Europe. However, by the Edwardian heyday of the south Wales coal industry many colliery companies were large enough to invest to an unprecedented degree in highly capitalized new colliery construction. A freshly laid out colliery on an ideal plan usually incorporated the same functional types of buildings as a colliery which had evolved more gradually, though there were variations according to local needs, finance, date and region. The principal building types found in the industry are discussed in separate sections of this book. The central structures were the headframes, or earlier winding gear, over the shafts. These were surrounded by their attached cover buildings, together with the pit banks which formed the shaft tops and the platforms or terraces from which coal was tipped into waggons or screens. Screens were used at most collieries by the late nineteenth century to sort and size coal, increasingly with mechanical assistance. From the end of the nineteenth century most large collieries also had large washery buildings.

Close to the pithead were a variety of buildings associated with generating power. At the end of the eighteenth century and through much of the nineteenth century, colliery sites were dominated by tall beam-engine houses housing mighty pumping-engines with a myriad of flimsy and variable wooden headframes attached. In the early nineteenth century the twin functions of pumping and winding were often combined. With the continual deepening of shafts (typically 180ft. (55 m.) in 1837 and 600ft. (183 m.)

The Edwardian Colliery at Oakdale was newly planned along organized lines with twin winding houses by a well-funded subsidiary of the long-established Tredegar Iron & Coal Company in 1908-10.

in 1875) more powerful winding-engines, and substantial steel headframes, were in use by the end of the nineteenth century. The winding-engine houses, with attached headframes, had then emerged as the most dominant shaft-head features, often with horizontal compound pumps in their basements, as at Marine and Llanover Hall Collieries. Their equivalent at drift mines were haulage engine houses. Other engine houses with specific functions were also grouped close to the shafts, notably fan houses (sometimes replacing earlier ventilation furnaces and their chimneys), and electricity generating, and compressor, houses to provide power for distribution to surface or underground machinery. In many of the collieries built after about 1900, some of these engine-powered functions were gathered under one roof, for example placing a generator in the same building as a winding-engine or, on the grandest scale, placing all the prime movers of a colliery in one huge engine hall, as was favoured by the Powell Duffryn company. In most cases before the age of electrification, a central range of boilers or enclosed boiler house and chimney adjacent to one of the main winding houses provided steam for the various engines around a colliery site. All collieries had stables for the ubiquitous horses used for haulage. Some of the larger collieries also had locomotive sheds for surface haulage, and engine houses to operate aerial ropeways for waste tipping.

An important group of surface building types was associated with the supply of materials for underground use. The workshops were the most important of these and could be extensive at the larger collieries, including electrical sections, foundries, engineering shops, fitting shops and sawmills, gathered in one or two buildings or dispersed around several. Stores buildings were usually separate in larger collieries for security reasons. Explosives stores were kept distant, with heavy brickwork and usually barrel-vaulted roofs to help reduce the dangers from accidental explosions.

Several building types were concerned with personnel. The lamp-room near the pithead was often a distinctive building type with queuing areas and

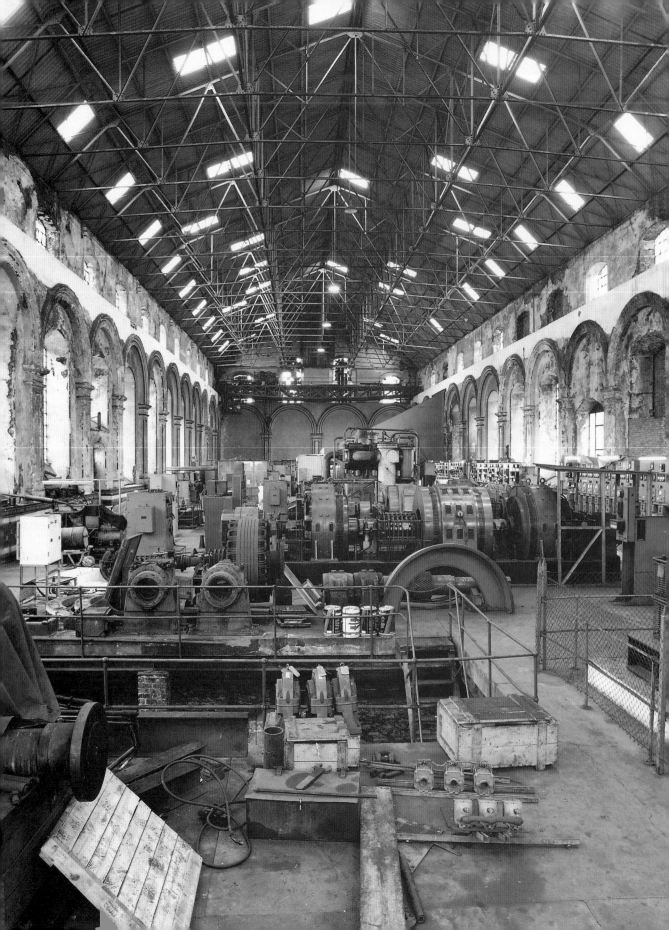

windows for lamps to be passed through. There were often several offices for different activities and different grades of staff and management. A manager's house was sometimes nearby. Pithead baths were introduced from the 1920s and became universal after nationalization, with distinctive designs developed by the architects of the Miners' Welfare Committee. They usually incorporated not only locker rooms and showers but a canteen, a medical centre and a mortuary. Larger mine rescue stations like those at Dinas, Crumlin and Loughor were always centrally placed to serve an area rather than sited at one colliery.

The major considerations governing the layout of new collieries is suggested in a series of articles by their designers. The first is by the Edwardian engineer, George G. Hann, who described his work at Penallta Colliery for the great Powell Duffryn Steam Coal Company.[1] The main determinant of the site, as in all other cases, was the presence of the coal measures, here thought to be *about 400 yards* [366m.] *to the south of the main synclinal which traverses the South Wales coalfield.'* A trial pit was sunk to locate the solid rock and the uppermost of the coal seams. Many of the eighteenth-century Swansea shafts were sunk on or immediately adjacent to faults so that the strata could be explored in all directions.

The next determinant of siting was the pattern of land ownership. At Penallta the only available large site was on a hillside, although Hann considered that *'it no doubt would have been preferable to have placed the shafts in the bottom of the basin.'*

The shaft site also had to be established, and maintained on solid and undisturbed ground. At Penallta the old workings of the Mynydd Islwyn seam *'approach within a very few yards of the west end of the main engine-house.'* At the slightly later Britannia Colliery a similar situation arose and the larger machinery had to be sited on huge concrete foundations to ensure that heavy vibration did not initiate subsidence.

Ideally, as at Penallta, the upcast and downcast

The large resources available to the Powell Duffryn Steam Coal Company at the height of the coal boom-fuelling the vast steamship fleets of the world-allowed it to build this long common engine hall housing all the surface machinery of the new Penallta Colliery (1906-09).

shafts should be aligned along the level width of the rising coal strata. The distance between the two shafts (210ft.(64m.)) *'being governed by the opposing requirements, of making a convenient arrangement at the pit bottoms and of reducing the distance to avoid long connecting headings for ventilation and for dealing with the water during the sinking.'*

Most colliery sites developed in more piecemeal fashion. The constricted valley sites of Wales resulted in many having long narrow layouts, often with extensive masonry revetment walls between the various parts of the colliery. At Penallta, *'the retaining wall against the sidings was altogether built of …Pennant stone…brought out of the shafts during the sinking.'* Indeed, it was claimed more generally that, *'As to the general arrangement of surface buildings, such as engine-houses, boilers, screens, etc., the area and disposition of the ground enclosed will largely determine the matter for each individual colliery'.*[2]

Such factors explain some of the variations found at Bedwas, whose construction was described in 1913. Otherwise the factors determining the design of this colliery were broadly the same as those that had determined the layout of Penallta, with some minor modifications. The siting of Bedwas alongside the Brecon and Merthyr Railway considerably eased the transport of the coal produced but restricted the length of the common engine-hall, with the result that the fan engine was located in an annex on the shaft side of the engine hall rather than at one end.[3]

Britannia Colliery, built for the Powell Duffryn Steam Coal Company in 1910-14, was the third designed by the Hann family of engineers within the space of a few years.[4] The confined site available for the construction of this pit resulted in it being the first colliery sunk and worked by electricity both in Wales and internationally (electricity-generating plant was first installed at collieries in Britain in 1882 and in Wales in 1890). Britannia first produced coal in 1914, just as the first all-electric collieries were also being completed in the other British coalfields.[5] There were none of the great ranks of uncovered steam-boilers so characteristic of the south Wales coal-field, neither was there the need for a large cooling pond or reservoir. Nor was there stabling for the horses used universally elsewhere for haulage: the whole output was carried on conveyor belts because horses had been unavailable at the beginning of the First World War when the pit was being sunk.

This revolution in motive power was facilitated by the development of power grids by the larger companies on the coalfield. Britannia had five feeder lines served by three sources of power. The surplus gas from the coke ovens of Bargoed Colliery, located 1.25 miles (2km.) up the Rhymney Valley, drove gas engines to generate electricity conveyed along two overhead lines of 0.25 sq. in. (1.6cm^2) section. The exhaust steam of the earlier Penallta Colliery drove two 3,000 kw. mixed pressure turbo-generators. These were each capable of generating 1,750 kw. on the exhaust steam from the engines powering Penallta Colliery and were installed to supply power to Britannia Colliery during the sinking of the shafts. Two 10,000 volt lines were carried three miles (4.8km.) north-eastwards to Britannia along one line of posts. In 1916, 30,000 volt power-lines were also extended much further westwards to the Middle Duffryn Power Station at Aberdare. The length of the power line was nine miles (14.5km.), comprising eight miles (12.9km.) of overhead power line and one mile (1.6km.) of underground cable. All the Powell Duffryn Collieries in the Cynon and Rhymney Valleys were thereby linked in a system that provided 16,000 kw. at peak times and produced an annual production of 75,000,000 units. The 2,190ft. (668m.) depth of shaft at Britannia, with an intended output of 360 tons per hour, meant that conventional winders producing 5,000 h.p. were needed. However, this was too great a load to be carried by the power generated simply from the waste of neighbouring collieries and two generator (Ilgner) sets with 30 ton flywheels and two 10,000 volt A.C. motors and variable voltage dynamos were installed, together with a storage battery of 117 cells. This stored power was sufficient on its own to raise the hopper, used in construction, up the shaft.

The two generating sets were placed in line with a total length of 102ft. (31.08m.), but as the workings in the house-coal seam belonging to a neighbouring colliery company had worked to within a short distance of the shafts it was necessary to place them on the heavily reinforced foundation described below.

Britannia was also connected to Bargoed Colliery

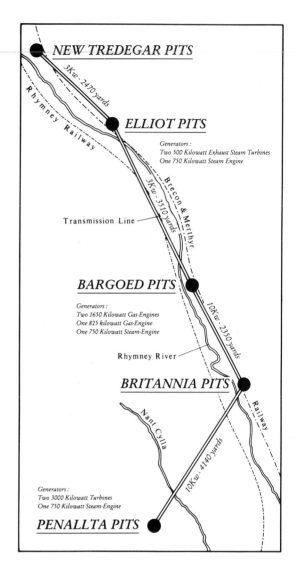

The development of electrical supply grids revolutionized power availability and reduced the infrastructure needed at such colliery sites as Britannia (1910-14). ('The Colliery Guardian', 26 July 1918)

by a 9in. (.23m.) diameter compressed air pipeline in case of failure of compressing equipment at either colliery, and to ease the economics of weekend and night working.

Modifications and expansions of the original layout of a colliery were, of course, commonplace. Existing shafts were often deepened for the working of new seams or for horizon mining of existing seams. Only rarely were existing winders found capable of handling increased loads and new depth duties, and the introduction of new equipment might involve extensions to boiler plants where steam was used, or alternatively a change over to electric winding.[6]

The differences in approach to colliery design and layout are clearly visible in the illustrations accompanying this chapter. The first photograph of Blaenserchan clearly shows the often severe constrictions of the topography. The level site of the original colliery was created by quarrying the hillside on the left of the photograph and dumping the spoil alongside. Later the site was extended to the right by a similar process. The site was widened into the valley, in the foreground of the photograph, by the expedient of tipping colliery spoil, and extra railway sidings were laid on the enlarged platform.

The two photographs of the buildings at Blaenserchan Colliery taken in the period 1975-79 show a colliery in transition. In fact this marked the middle of three diversions of coal output away from the Blaenserchan pithead, so that it might be raised instead at adjacent pitheads. In 1977 this was to be Abertillery New Mine. The cleared area on the left foreground of the first photograph seems to have been the site of successively larger workshops and stores, already standing by 1877 and enlarged by 1917.[7] To accompany the working amalgamation with Abertillery prefabricated sheds provided larger accommodation again.

In 1877 the terrace on the southern hillside of Cwm Du encompassed only the site of the shaft visible in the foreground and its surrounding area. By 1917 the colliery had been deepened , and the terrace had been extended westwards to accommodate another shaft, on the staggered alignment necessitated by the shape of the terrace.[8] The buildings, albeit of differing dates, were built in a style common to large parts of the south Wales coalfield at the end of the nineteenth and the beginning of the twentieth century. This had the mass of the walls built of rusticated Pennant sandstone with all the dressings of the buildings, i.e. quoins and the semicircular-headed and circular openings, executed in yellow engineering brick. An apparent homogeneity in style belied the piecemeal development of such collieries.

The two photographs also illustrate no fewer than four stages in the development of the ventilation of the colliery. The shaft in the background replaced the downcast shaft of the adjacent Llanerch Colliery in providing air through the deepened workings to the original upcast shaft in the foreground, recognizable by its airtight casing within the headgear. Beyond the headgear the housing for the original fan is visible, and to the right, in the earlier photograph, is the gabled secondary fan-engine house with the distinctive squat, square stack of the fan vent (or évasée) clearly visible. On the later photograph, the fan-engine house has been crudely converted, giving it a flat roof and infilling the arched window, with its elegant cast-iron frame, to produce a square four-light window. The modern fan with its concrete casing and distinctive wedge-like steel vent is an obvious replacement of the old square stack.

The corrugated shed beyond the fan vent in the earlier photograph carried the mine tram (or dram) railway circuit from the upcast shaft over the main railway siding which lay at a level below that of the colliery terrace (a relationship typical of south Wales, and seen also in the photographs of Celynen North and Oakdale Collieries). The diversion of the Blaenserchan output through other collieries made this arrangement redundant and by 1978 the building carrying the tram circuit over the site of the railway tracks had disappeared.

This use of some sites for access and others for bringing up coal was typical of the later days of the south Wales coalfield. The extent of the interconnections may be demonstrated at Blaenserchan. In 1969 its coal was routed southwards underground through Tirpentwys to Hafodyrynys Colliery; from 1977 Blaenserchan coal went to Abertillery New Mine, and from 1985 it went westwards through Six Bells and on to Marine Colliery.

The illustrations of Celynen North and Oakdale contrast large-scale planning and more piecemeal growth. The two engine houses attached to the Oakdale shafts were identical and part of a planned layout of a large colliery and attached model settlement: a large investment. The scale of the horseshoe layout of the garden village at Oakdale, with its central grand avenue, shops and social centre at the heart, and the colliery beyond, it is clearly visible in the aerial photograph. At Celynen North it is obvious that more piecemeal growth, and modest investment, produced engine houses attached to twin shafts of differing dates.

Some of the most impressive planned layouts consisted of the large engine-halls and subsidiary workshop blocks built by the Powell Duffryn Steam Coal Company, and others, in the Edwardian period. Illustrated is the great engine-hall of the last steam-powered colliery of Powell Duffryn, at Penallta, where all the machinery previously in scattered and disparate engine houses was brought together under one roof - two winding-engines, compressors, generators and fans. The same company's next large colliery at Britannia (Pengam) was similar but electrically powered. The plan, obtained from British Coal, shows the integrated layout achieved. The engine hall at Llantrisant Colliery has been long deserted, but it still retains its travelling crane which could lift all the heavy machinery conveniently situated in a single hall. The large openings in the floor gave access to the machine foundations and services, which also had access from a railway line running into the basement.

The colliery baths and medical centres of the 1920s and 1930s were important additions to earlier colliery layouts, and were distinctive both in architecture and siting. The accompanying aerial view of Oakdale Colliery shows the original pit layout in, and just above, the valley bottom. The washery is visible on the valley bottom, towards the top of the photograph. Nearer, and on the valley side, are the twin colliery shafts, flanked on either side by the winding-engine houses. Nearer again is the common engine-hall with ventilating-fan vent on its right-hand side. On the car-park closer to the camera again are the colliery offices, and the large white building nearest the camera is the baths block, added to the colliery at a later date.

The large resources of the National Coal Board were later to produce several large-scale planned layouts, such as that at Maerdy ('Mardy'), which replaced the somewhat jumbled earlier layout there.

Maerdy was rebuilt in the late 1940s - the first material realization of the bright new future planned by the newly nationalized coal industry. Mining and mining employment in the Rhondda were intended to be revived with the use of the continental method of large-scale coal working known as 'horizon mining.' Over £5,000,000 was invested from 1947 until the scheme reached full production ten years later.[9]

The two shafts of the original colliery on the site had been sunk in 1893 and 1914 respectively.[10] Both shafts had engine houses of disparate design extending towards the hillside; the new layout turned the head-gear and winding-engine house through 90 degrees as part of a scheme to align neatly all the colliery buildings along the hillside. There had previously been a jumble of winder, compressor houses and other ancillary buildings between the two engine houses, with the screens buildings extending beyond the upper shaft. In the new layout parallel ranges next to the lower shaft housed the workshops and the lamp-room/administrative and office blocks. To the south, the line of these was continued by the baths and canteen blocks. By the time the accompanying photograph was taken, the washery that had stood in the foreground had already been demolished following the establishment of an underground connection to the coal-preparation plant at Tower Colliery in the Cynon Valley in 1986. Before this the Maerdy site, restricted by its position at the top of a narrow and deep valley, had been widened with the retaining walls seen in the photograph. The extensive railway sidings in the valley bottom were so designed that a full days supply of empty railway wagons could be held there. There was also the capacity to hold a day and a half's output in filled railway wagons. This was considered necessary mainly to guard against the effects of severe winters.[11] Maerdy Colliery closed in 1990 and has been demolished, but at the time of writing Tower is mothballed awaiting a decision about its future. The output from Tower was brought to the surface some distance away from the earlier pithead via a drift or slant (an inclined tunnel) driven in 1958-59 below an earlier coal-mining landscape. This section of the very dispersed surface site, set over extensive underground workings, includes some of the coal-preparation plant

The large resources of the nationalized coal industry allowed substantial replanning of integrated coalfields. The two photographs opposite illustrate Blaenserchan Colliery at a time of change in 1975-79; buildings were replaced or rebuilt as Abertillery New Mine was developed as the new outlet for coal from the area.

and a long conveyor-belt down to the disposal point. Such sloping access tunnels have always been an important part of the south Wales mining scene and can still be seen in use at the Betws Mine.

Broader spreads of surface buildings, planned on rectangular grids, were built on two of the National Coal Board's new anthracite sinkings in the 1950s. These were at Cynheidre (completed 1954-56) and Abernant (shaft completed 1958), but are now closed.

The architectural design of colliery buildings was subject to many influences of period, ownership, region, and function. Most were simple and solid with only a nod here and there towards architectural style, such as brick corbelling, pilasters or interior tiling. Regional differences were apparent in the early use of brick in the Wrexham area, the small scale of buildings in the shallow mines of Pembrokeshire, or the massive grandeur of the major Rhondda concerns. The ownership of collieries also created differences. The Powell Duffryn company, for example, had a house style which makes even their offices or their engine houses recognizable; the Ocean combine appears to have continued building in stone long after brick or concrete were commonplace, as at Deep Navigation where the winding-engine houses were rebuilt in stone in the 1930s. Some buildings were treated differently from others owing to their function. Washeries, for example, were usually constructed from about World War I following a characteristic system of bolted steel frames infilled with brick panels to withstand vibration and afford flexibility for machinery. Pithead baths were heavily influenced in style by Modernism. Their asymmetric plans, plenum towers and horizontal emphases were introduced by the Miners' Welfare Committee architects and became normal at large collieries from the 1920s.

The most important variations in the design of colliery buildings were brought about over time during the industrial revolution and later. Naturally, colliery buildings became more sophisticated between the eighteenth and twentieth centuries. Eighteenth-century pithead buildings are shown in many contemporary illustrations to be of timber or rubble with thatched roofs, but the earliest well-constructed stone buildings were the pumping-engine houses built following the first successful Newcomen pump built at Dudley in 1712. The use of flimsy building materials continued into the nineteenth century, particularly on smaller collieries such as those on the tiny Anglesey coalfield. Here in 1803-06 two water 'whimseys' (i.e. pithead waterwheel winders) were protected by a willow structure costing five shillings.[12] The common use of corrugated iron or steel for many colliery buildings has continued to the present day. However, most substantial colliery buildings by the early nineteenth century were built of dressed local sandstone and were monumental in design, becoming increasingly so as the century passed. This continued up until the last quarter of the century and can be seen in buildings like the Scott's Pit engine-house of 1817 and the Lewis Merthyr complex of the 1880s. The latter indicates also the different treatment often given to buildings according to their function. Winding-engine houses were always considered the buildings of highest status in a colliery, and at Lewis Merthyr these were all of stone, whereas the adjacent buildings were stone with brick dressings. Frequently, engine houses also had plasterwork and tiled dados inside, as at Penallta or Llanbradach, built at the turn of the century.

From the 1880s colliery buildings generally became much larger as many mines became deeper and employed greater numbers. The largest were the enormous common engine-halls favoured by the Powell Duffryn company after about 1906. Brick became used generally for dressings to windows and doors and often also for pilasters and quoins, as at Penallta, or the stone and brick winding-house at Plas Power Colliery of 1875 which was precocious in its use of brick owing to its proximity to the advanced brick industry of the Wrexham area. In Clwyd, all-brick colliery buildings seem to have been introduced by the 1890s, but the first wholly brick complexes in South Wales seem to date from the early twentieth century, as at Crumlin Navigation built in 1907.

The Colliery Guardian noted in 1920 [13] that 'the Welsh Navigation Steam Coal Company' had opened a brickworks after acquiring Coed Ely Colliery in 1911 and all the new buildings were completely of brick, whereas the buildings erected by Henry Lewis during the sinking of the pit in 1906 were built from Pennant sandstone taken from the mine.

In 1907 the French engineer, T.J.Gueritte, lectured

to the North of England Institute of Mining and Mechanical Engineers on 'Ferro-concrete and its Applications'.[14] Reinforced concrete began to be used extensively in British mines in 1910 and the Powell Duffryn Steam Coal Company's engineer, Mr. Griffiths Abraham, designed concrete airtight pithead chambers for the Penallta Colliery (1910). Gueritte considered the new material particularly suitable for such structures which, when made of steel, could easily develop leaks from the incessant vibration of the winding machinery. At Penallta this structure was 130ft. (39.6m.) long and 30ft. (9.1m.) wide. Similar considerations, and concern over possible subsidence near the pithead, led to the use of the new material for machinery foundations. One of its earliest applications in Britain was in the foundation raft for two Ilgner flywheel motor generator sets at Britannia Colliery. The raft was 102ft. (31m.) in length, 20ft. (6.1m.) in width and 17ft. (5.2m.) in thickness. A contemporary description noted that:

'The total weight of the machinery exceeds 200 tons, each of the two flywheels weighing 30 tons. They run normally at 500 revolutions per minute, but can be slowed down to run at 425 revolutions if necessary. The continual speeding-up and slowing-down causes severe stresses in the foundations, but owing to the scientifically arranged network of steel rods throughout the ferro-concrete work, no ill-effects accrue.' [15]

The reinforced-concrete machinery foundation at Britannia Colliery sat within a traditional building of Pennant sandstone with red-brick dressings. Similar traditional, or composite, structures were used elsewhere in the coalfield in this period. The surviving colliery engine-hall surveyed at Lower Navigation (Talywaun), Abersychan, Gwent, had traditional enclosing walls of red brick seated on a reinforced-concrete foundation with concrete pillars supporting the machinery floor, itself also made of reinforced concrete. The earlier tradition of timber pillars was reflected in the concrete pillars having neatly chamfered corners.

A significant series of structures constructed totally out of reinforced concrete in south Wales was noted in *The Colliery Guardian* for 1919.[16] The bunkers at the Powell Duffryn's Bargoed Colliery were 110ft. (33.5m.) high and held 1,000 tons of coal. Those at

Port Talbot held 21,000 tons. Surviving until recently was the unusual circular concrete bunker of the Powell Duffryn Company at Britannia Colliery. This was 95ft. (29m.) high, 32ft (9.75m.) in diameter, with a storage compartment 66ft (20m.) high and holding some 1,500 tons of coal. The circular structure, designed by the Powell Duffryn engineer, Ivor Williams, was considered to be a cheap means of constructing such a structure. The *Mining Engineer* for 1919-20 congratulated him *'on the very artistic effect given to such a utilitarian structure by the provision of a light string course in the right position.'*[17]

Bargoed Colliery also had an early undercover reservoir constructed in concrete, holding some 80,000 gallons.[18] By 1919 the use of concrete in south Wales extended well beyond the pioneering efforts of the large Powell Duffryn Steam Coal Company. An advertisement in that year promoted the products of Simon-Carves Ltd., of Manchester and listed the Oakdale Navigation Collieries Ltd. (near Blackwood) and the Great Western Colliery (near Pontypridd) as two of five colliery companies using their products in Britain and India.[19]

The nationalization of the coal industry on 1 January 1947 brought with it a host of changes to the physical appearance and operation of collieries, especially where they were wholly rebuilt or built new. In the early years after nationalization the influence of 'Modernism' was felt strongly in all new buildings, not just in the design of pithead baths as previously. The new power hall at Point of Ayr built in 1952 had a wide shell concrete roof of parabolic waves, reminiscent of Festival of Britain building, above long strip windows. Maerdy ('Mardy') was rebuilt in 1948-53 around cubic winding engine-houses with continuous glazing and rooflights more reminiscent of the work of the Bauhaus architects in Germany than anything previously built in Britain. Some new structures were introduced in the following years, such as the great tower-mounted winders used at Abernant and Cynheidre in the 1950s.

From about the 1960s the early architectural aspirations of the National Coal Board gave way to cheaper designs for an industry in relative decline. The buildings at Betws, begun in the 1970s, were unambitious compared with their predecessors. Brick and concrete buildings have increasingly given way to corrugated covers over steel frames, as at Tower washery. The small private mines of the post war period have been characterized by ephemeral structures such as portakabins and steel sheds rather than the major buildings characteristic of the great period of Welsh coalmining in the nineteenth and early twentieth centuries.

The remainder of this book describes many buildings which were recorded before demolition, and also features some which still survive as a testament to this dominant Welsh industry's important past.

References

1   G.G. Hann, 'The Sinking and Equipping of Penallta Colliery', *Proceedings of the South Wales Institute of Engineers* XXVII (1910-11), pp.47-69. The family name 'Hann' suggests that this family of engineers had German connections that may well have influenced them in introducing the common engine-hall that was already in use in German-speaking Europe. The Zentralmaschinen-haus of 1802 at Zollern 2/4 Colliery in Dortmund is said to be the earliest of this type (p.c. Dr.Walter Buschmann, Landschaftsverband, Rheinland).

2   E.L. Hann, 'The Sinking and Equipping of Bedwas Colliery', *The Colliery Guardian* CVI (5 Sept. 1913), pp.473-78.

3   E.L. Hann, 'The Sinking and Equipping of Bedwas Colliery', *Proceedings of the South Wales Institute of Engineers* XXIX (1913), pp.330-49.

4   G. Hann, 'The Britannia Colliery, Pengam, Mon'. *The Colliery Guardian* CXVI (26 July 1918), pp.173-75.

5   Electricity generating plant was introduced at Trafalgar Colliery in the Forest of Dean, Gloucestershire, in 1882 (R. Thornes, *Images of Industry*: COAL, (Swindon, 1994)), p.54. The first non-lighting use of electricity in a colliery in Wales was in 1890 at Newbridge in the Rhondda. Powell Duffryn led the way to fuller electrification with the introduction of electric winders in 1906 at Old Duffryn and Abercwmboi Collieries (A.V.Jones, 'The Early Development of Electrical Engineering in the south Wales Coalfield', ms. copy with R.Keen, National Trust).

Maritime Colliery, Pontypridd, had been electrified in 1908 but had been sunk with steam-engines. It is said that Britannia Colliery was the first to be both sunk and completely operated by electricity, not only in Britain but also in the rest of the world. Early German electricallly operated collieries such as Zollern 2/4 in Dortmund had steam engines on site to drive their electrical generators (R.S.Stevens in papers presented on 'Britannia Colliery' and 'Ward Leonard Colliery Winders' to the fifth and sixth annual conferences of the Institution of Electrical Engineers on The History of Elecrical Engineering (1977 & 1978) and also the same author's 'An Apology for Electric Mine Winders', *South East Wales Industrial Archaeology Society Transactions* (1979)). Britannia is given as the first all-electric pit in Britain in A.Hill, *Coal Mining: A Technological Chronogy. 1700-1950* (Sheffield, 1991). By 1921 55 per cent of the south Wales coalfield was electrified.

6   G. L. Kerr, *Practical Coal-mining: a manual for managers, under-managers, colliery engineers, and others* (London, 1922), p.699; E. Mason, *Practical Coal Mining* (London, 4th. ed. 1954), vol.2, p.643.

7   Ordnance Survey, 1:2,500 Monmouthshire XVIII.13, editions of 1877 and 1917.

8   ibid and J. Cornwell, *Collieries of Western Gwent* (Cowbridge, 1983), pp.36-37.

9   M. Tutton, 'Report on Mardy Colliery', MS. in RCAHMW, 1991.

10 W.G. Thomas, *Welsh Coal Mines* (Cardiff, 1986), p.34.

11 Tutton, 'Report on Mardy Colliery'.

12 T.M. Bassett and G. James, 'Coalmining in Anglesey', *Anglesey Antiquarian Society Transactions* (1969-70), pp.137-163.

13 'Coed Ely Colliery', *The Colliery Guardian CXX* (13 Aug. 1920), pp.445-47.

14 T.J. Gueritte, 'The Applications of Ferro-Concrete in Mines', *The Colliery Guardian* CXVIII (24 Dec. 1919), pp.1909-11.

15 ibid.

16 ibid.

17 T.J. Gueritte, 'The Applications of Ferro-Concrete in Mines', *The Mining Engineer* LVIII (1919-20), *pp.184-211.*

18 ibid.

19 Advertisement in the *The Colliery Guardian,* CXVII, (17 April 1919), p.911.

The large profits generated from the steam-coal exports of the Edwardian period allowed such substantial concerns as the Tredegar Iron and Coal Company's Oakdale subsidiary to extend ordered large-scale planning from the Oakdale Colliery (1908-10) to the adjoining planned layout of the miners' 'garden village' of 1909-24. On the aerial view opposite, the colliery itself is visible beyond Oakdale village to the top left of the photograph. The communal facilities included the Oakdale Workmen's Institute which was removed in 1989 from the centre of the 'horseshoe' for re-erection at the Welsh Folk Museum.

(Above) This aerial photograph of Oakdale Colliery shows how the original layout (1908-10) was amended by the addition of miners' baths (foreground) on a different alignment.

(Below) The resources of The National Coal Board allowed new and large-scale engineering works to proceed including the amalgamation of pits and the driving of large inclined tunnels ('drifts') to bring up merged colliery outputs, as here at Tower Colliery; the drift (1958-59) emerged into the earthworks of an earlier nineteenth-century mining landscape.

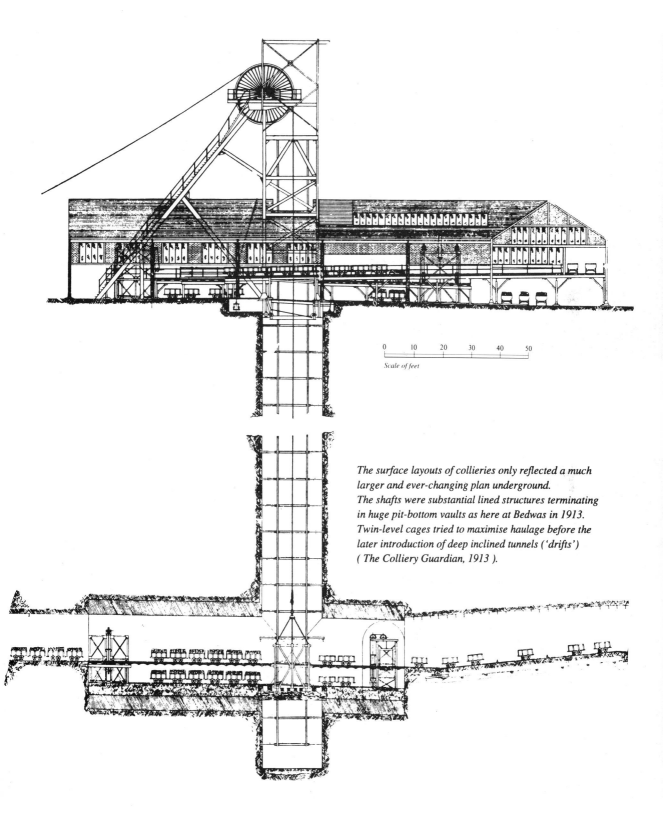

0   10   20   30   40   50

Scale of feet

The surface layouts of collieries only reflected a much
larger and ever-changing plan underground.
The shafts were substantial lined structures terminating
in huge pit-bottom vaults as here at Bedwas in 1913.
Twin-level cages tried to maximise haulage before the
later introduction of deep inclined tunnels ('drifts')
(The Colliery Guardian, 1913).

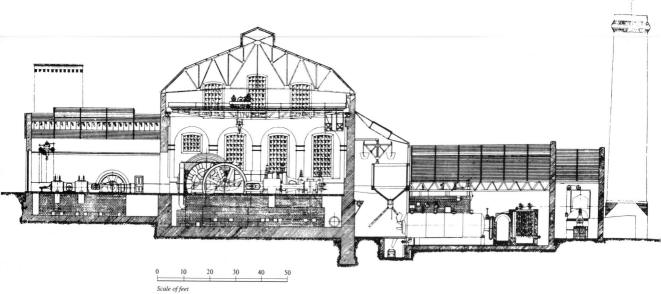

The resemblance between these cross-sections of the great Edwardian engine halls at Bedwas (top) and Penallta (bottom) reflects the fact that they are both works by the Hann dynasty of colliery engineers. Identical roof-trusses spanned long four-bay wide halls with thirty-ton capacity travelling cranes available for maintaining all the colliery machinery available in the halls. Bedwas had its compound steam-engines supported by large piers of brick whilst those at Penallta are of mass concrete. The restricted Bedwas site resulted in the fan engine having to be sited alongside, rather than in, the engine hall. ('The Proceedings of the South Wales Institute of Engineers', 1910-11 & 'The Colliery Guardian', 1913).

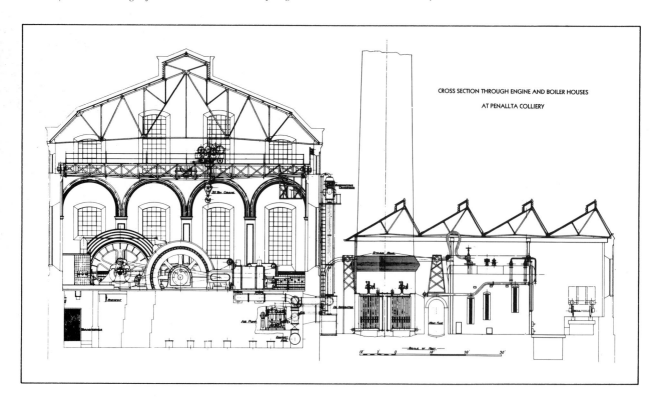

CROSS SECTION THROUGH ENGINE AND BOILER HOUSES

AT PENALLTA COLLIERY

Maerdy ('Mardy') Colliery was the first new combined mine project developed by the National Coal Board soon after its formation in 1948-53 when Maerdy (Rhondda Fach) was linked to Bwllfa No.1 Colliery, two and a half miles away over the mountain, in the Dare Valley. The old winding-houses of 1893 and 1914 were replaced by the cubic modern ranges seen in the photograph. The continuous glazing and rooflights of its architecture was more reminiscent of the work of the Bauhaus architects in Germany than anything previously built in Britain.

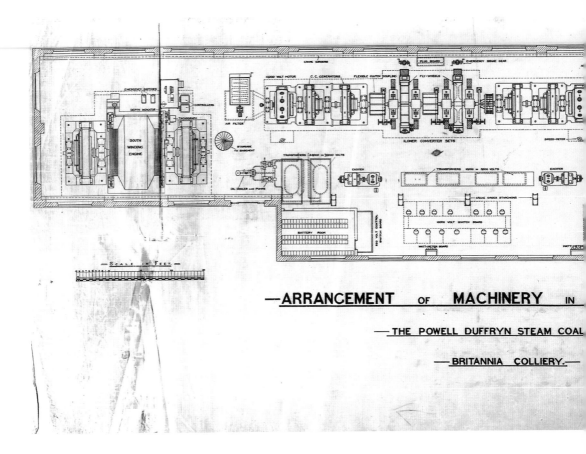

ARRANGEMENT OF MACHINERY IN

THE POWELL DUFFRYN STEAM COAL

BRITANNIA COLLIERY.

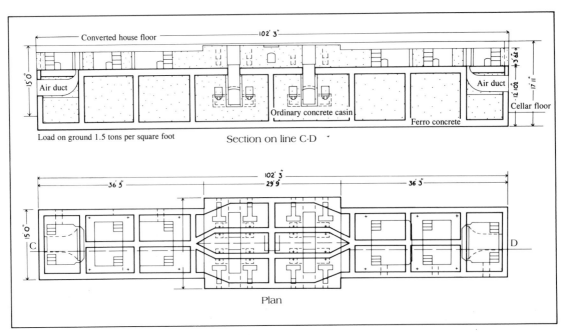

Converted house floor

Air duct

Air duct

Cellar floor

Ordinary concrete casin

Ferro concrete

Load on ground 1.5 tons per square foot

Section on line C-D

Plan

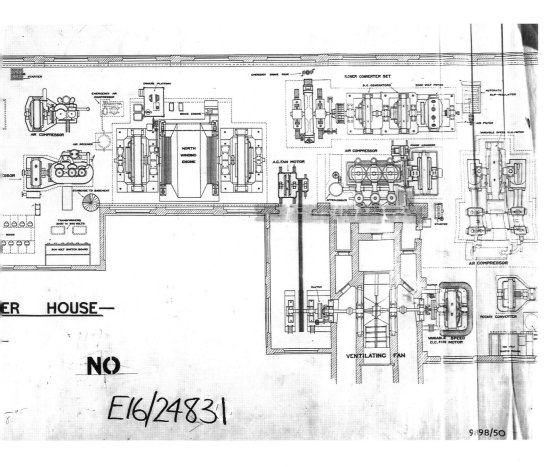

ER HOUSE—

NO

E16/24831

9898/50

The construction of Britannia Colliery (1910-14) included many revolutionary elements. It succeeded Penallta (1906-09) in having one of the first large common engine-halls in Britain, but here a restricted site resulted in the decision that this should be the first all-electric pit in Wales (and indeed the world), with power generated by existing steam-engines at Penallta and engines elsewhere.
To maintain a constant electrical current large flywheels were required on the Ilgner electrical convertors; to lessen vibration and to prevent the whole structure subsiding into nearby earlier workings, these were sited on a very large reinforced-concrete foundation (pictured left). The new material of reinforced concrete was also used for the high circular coal-storage bunker (pictured right); the Powell Duffryn engineer, Ivor Williams, was commended in the contemporary engineering literature for its 'very artistic effect' (British Coal drawings (Glamorgan Archives Service); 'The Colliery Guardian', 1918 and 'The Mining Engineer', 1919-20)

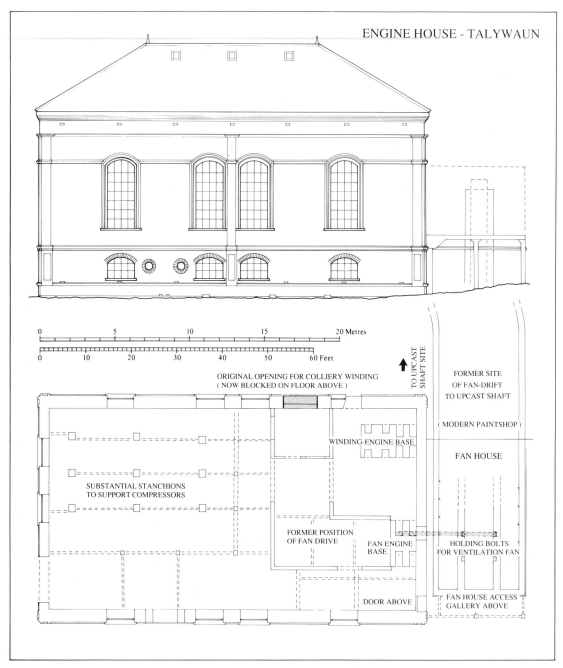

ENGINE HOUSE - TALYWAUN

0   5   10   15   20 Metres

0   10   20   30   40   50   60 Feet

TO UPCAST SHAFT SITE

ORIGINAL OPENING FOR COLLIERY WINDING
(NOW BLOCKED ON FLOOR ABOVE)

FORMER SITE
OF FAN-DRIFT
TO UPCAST SHAFT

(MODERN PAINTSHOP)

WINDING-ENGINE BASE

FAN HOUSE

SUBSTANTIAL STANCHIONS
TO SUPPORT COMPRESSORS

FORMER POSITION
OF FAN DRIVE

FAN ENGINE
BASE

HOLDING BOLTS
FOR VENTILATION FAN

DOOR ABOVE

FAN HOUSE ACCESS
GALLERY ABOVE

Reinforced concrete was first used in conjunction with brick in composite structures such as that surviving in the colliery engine-hall at Lower Navigation Colliery,Talywaun, Abersychan, (Survey drawing compiled by Myfanwy Eaves and Jonathan Gill of the Ironbridge Institute, and Royal Commission staff) where a substantial brick building sits on a large concrete raft supporting internal concrete columns and machine bases topped by a reinforced-concrete floor at the main engine-hall level, and with an external lower concrete frame for the colliery ventilation fan. This contrasts with the bold unadorned reinforced-concrete tower built to bunker coal at Bargoed Colliery in 1913 (pictured opposite). Some of the larger collieries, as here, had their own adjacent coking works, the last works to survive is at Cwm, which is presently being recorded by the Royal Commission.

(Above): Valleyside situations, and the need to load coal into railway wagons at lower levels, resulted in many collieries having pit-banks revetted by huge retaining walls, as here at Celynen North.

(Left): Late nineteenth-and early twentieth-century collieries often had open ranges of boilers necessary to drive the multiple powerful steam-engines on each colliery site, as at Morlais Colliery (1889-91: upper left). Electric power advanced with the first all-electric pit in Wales (and the world) at Britannia (1910-14). The switchgear pictured at lower left stood in one of the large cubic halls of Maerdy Colliery (1948-53), built on a grand scale by the then confident and newly formed National Coal Board

Underground structures in shifting coal measures are unlikely to last for ever. This view of Lady Windsor Colliery shows the distortion caused to the steel supporting rings of a gate roadway by an underground collapse in 1982 and explains why rock-bolting is deemed as effective as free-standing supports in trying to temporarily hold back these irresistible forces. (British Coal)

Collieries Underground

Enormous technological strides had transformed the ill-lit, gaseous, unstable and constricted series of irregular tunnels that formed an average coal mine early in the nineteenth century into the modern colliery with its bright lighting, good ventilation, large well-supported roadways and carefully planned layout, where safety for the miners has latterly been of paramount concern. Several factors provided the impetus for such a transition: the need to increase output considerably during the years of the coal boom in the late nineteenth and early twentieth centuries, and public pressure and legislation in the wake of countless minor accidents and major horrific disasters involving great loss of life. Since nationalization in 1947 there has been the recognition that swift and extensive mechanization was the only way that the British coal industry, in Wales as elsewhere, could stand any chance of competing in the international marketplace.

In south Wales, until about the middle of the nineteenth century, coal was won by working surface outcrops or *patches*, or by driving levels into the steep valley sides to intersect with or follow the seams. Shafts were sunk only as a last resort when other methods of reaching the coal were impractical; they were expensive and troublesome and could only be worked on a large scale with appropriate ventilation, winding and pumping (each dealt with in later chapters) to control the inherent problems of deep mines. Coal was worked from numerous small mines without the capital, or the need, to invest in sophisticated equipment and techniques. This had the effect of retarding the progress of mining technology so that by 1850 south Wales generally was considered to be lagging behind best practice elsewhere. However, the easily accessible shallow coal deposits eventually became exhausted; the necessity to sink deep shafts and solve the attendant problems, coupled with new ideas from migrant miners, legislation to improve safety, and the establishment in 1857 of the South Wales Institute of Engineers (creating an information exchange and debating forum) led to radical changes and great expansion in the industry in the second half of the nineteenth century.[1]

The north Wales coalfield covered a much smaller area than that in the south, and its exploitation peaked and declined much earlier. The seams are thinner, deeper and more fragmented than the richly-endowed south and this, coupled with geographical factors, has affected the development of the industry. Coal had been worked from shallow pits since the medieval period until the mid-eighteenth century when better communications and expansion of the iron industry attracted entrepreneurs with capital, particularly from the nearby mining areas of England, to equip and operate mines with the latest machinery. Steam power played an increasingly important role from 1775 when James Watt took out his patent for pumping-engines and the use of steam for pumping and winding the deep shafts had become widespread by the mid-nineteenth century. By then, however, coalmining was already in slow decline, partially offset by the creation of new local markets but hastened by the inexorable transfer of industries from the north to the more attractive coalfield then developing in south Wales.[2]

The traditional way of working deep coal in Wales was by *pillar and stall*, a centuries-old technique whereby chambers were excavated in the seam leaving supporting pillars of coal. The other main method, *longwall* mining, was devised in Shropshire in the seventeenth century but John Nixon later encountered much opposition in introducing longwall working to south Wales.[3] Its use spread rapidly after 1860 where underground conditions were suitable; it was a less wasteful method and allowed better circulation of ventilation air through the workings. Two parallel headings, known as the main and tail gateways, were driven from a main roadway, one on either side of the area of coal or *panel* to be removed. A cross-tunnel was bored between the heading ends, and coal cut from the long face exposed, either away from the main roadway (advancing) or towards it (retreating). In the days of hand-cutting and early mechanization, longwall mining was done on a twenty-four-hour cycle: one shift would cut coal and fire explosives, the next would load coal onto trams or conveyers, and during the third shift *packers* supported the roof behind while *panners* dismantled and reassembled the railway or conveyor nearer the coalface. Early attempts to mechanize parts of the process included devising compressed-air and electrically-powered coal-cutters and the shaking conveyor. In south Wales, one reason for the limited application of such early technical advances was that poor geological conditions favoured the continuation of manual working, and coalface mechanization made little impact in the area. In 1913, the year of peak production of coal in Wales, only 1 per cent was cut by machines. However, in the late 1940s the Anderson Boyes Company's Meco-Moore power cutter-loader, developed from a 1930s design, was installed in a Welsh Colliery (Penallta)[4]. This was the first effective machine to cut and load the coal simultaneously. Following this success, the plough and the flexible armoured conveyor were introduced from Germany in 1950 and revolutionized longwall mining. The plough, suited to the soft south Wales coal, was driven along the face and ripped coal straight onto the conveyor as a continuous operation. Also in 1950 James Anderton's Disc Shearer appeared which, with the Anderson Boyes' Trepanner, were highly successful non-cyclic cutting and loading machines.[5] Used with the armoured flexible conveyor and self-advancing hydraulic roof supports, these machines enabled coaling to proceed without interruption; very powerful versions of such systems are in universal use today where longwall mining is employed. These are virtually 'one-man' operations, where cutting and loading are carried out simultaneously and the conveyor and roof supports moved hydraulically, often from a nearby computerized control panel.

Fundamental to the success of underground mining operations, especially at the working face, is control of the roof. The access levels and drainage adits of early drift-mines were generally hewn through rock without additional support, but where it was required timber props and beams were cut and wedged individually to fit the rock strata. This practice continued until recently, although the strength of such a system was limited, if not unreliable, and required a considerable deployment of manpower to install and maintain. For more permanent applications, such as major drainage levels and main roadways, stone or brick-arched roofs were laboriously constructed. As early as the eighteenth century there were brick-arched mining levels at Swansea over one mile (1.6km.) long. Steel props began to replace timber, but a significant advance was the reusable hydraulic prop, introduced in about 1945[6] as a spin-off from war-time hydraulic technology, which developed into the sophisticated system of self-moving roof supports essential to the efficient working of modern collieries. Since their introduction in the late 1960s, roadheading machines have been employed where appropriate to cut the face of headings and remove the spoil by conveyors. Standard, commercially available, prefabricated steel-arched supports are assembled as excavation continues, backed by such linings as corrugated steel sheeting, although timber is still used, as are wire mesh panels, particularly where the geology allows rock-bolting to be employed. Rock-bolting, where even wooden or plastic bolts can be used so as not to damage coal-cutting machinery, gives great economies in cost and is a modern trend in roof support, having been introduced from the mines of the United States of America.

Transport of coal to the shaft bottom, sometimes over several miles of undulating roadway with numerous junctions, has been a significant problem since the early days of drift-mining. Excessive lengths of haulage were a contributory factor leading to the adoption of deep mining with vertical shafts. The haulage of coal trams in early mines by children and horses gradually gave way in the late nineteenth century to mechanical systems powered by steam, compressed air and (almost universally nowadays) electricity, although horses continued to be used extensively until recently, and indeed are still at work in some small pits. Despite mechanical haulage being undoubtedly cheaper and more efficient to operate, it was difficult to find a satisfactory alternative to the horse that was both effective and safe. The problems of piping steam from surface boilers to underground engines were great, yet installing boilers underground near the haulage engines created other difficulties. Compressed air and later electric power were certainly more suitable than steam, and were eventually widely applied to haulages. For example, an electric haulage system installed at United National Collieries in the Rhondda was 30 per cent faster than the steam haulage it replaced, produced no corrosive exhaust fumes, and by removing the steam pipe from the shaft a second cage could be installed.[7] At Britannia Colliery, sunk in 1910-14, it was decided from the outset that electric or compressed-air-powered conveyors and haulages would be employed exclusively, marking a significant technological advance,[8] although compressed-air haulages had been applied in south Wales since 1857.[9] Locomotive working by adhesion only is limited underground to about 1 in 30, ordinary conveyor belts have a maximum working angle of about 1 in 6, but rope or chain haulage can be used successfully over a wide range of conditions.[10] Rope haulage with trams is common as it is relatively cheap to install and flexible in use; almost any gradients and sharp changes in horizontal direction can be accommodated.

The process of colliery mechanization was relatively slow, partly as a result of the fragmented ownership of the coalfields and the small scale of operations prior to nationalization; south Wales suffered additionally from geological problems. Once the commitment to mechanize was made, however, its march was inexorable, if erratic. The awesome forces made available by the new primary and secondary movers - steam, compressed air, electricity and hydraulic power - enabled deeper shafts to be sunk, haulages to be longer and more coal to be cut. As demand encouraged the expansion of mines, and as they increased in size and complexity, so better ventilation and more powerful pumps, winders and compressors were required. Their introduction in turn allowed the mines to develop further. Different techniques and working practices had to be established to enable full advantage to be taken of this new technology. In some cases the mechanical equipment was already available but had not been fully exploited for reasons of conservatism, mistrust, or plain lack of money; for example, a coal-cutting machine was devised as long ago as 1761,[11] yet hand-cutting was still in regular use in some mines until well into the 1950s. It was only after 1947, when capital was made available to modernize the industry, that mechanization of the coalface progressed significantly.

Accidents were rife during the early period of mechanization; there were of course considerably more men employed in the new and much larger pits where application of the latest technological innovations exposed shortcomings in other machines or techniques not so well advanced. Every mishap also played a grim part in leading to improvements - even such fairly recent events as the Aberfan Tip disaster have spurred improvements in the industry.[12]

In modern times safety has been a prime consideration of underground working, not only in the way that operations were carried out but in the design and layout of the mines and their equipment. The extensive use of electricity for lighting, replacing the safety lamp which superseded naked flame illumination, contributed greatly to the improvement of the working environment. Comparatively sophisticated technology, such as electronic air-monitoring systems, remotely controlled video cameras and radio communication, is now commonplace in modern collieries. However, the rate of introduction of cheap and technologically simple ideas to improve safety in mines - such as the miners' safety lamp (resistance to its adoption was most notable in north Wales), dust suppression by water sprays, and the use of stone dust as an explosion retardant, was highly variable even between collieries operating under similar conditions in the same coalfield.

References:

1   J.H.Morris and L.J.Williams, *The South Wales Coal Industry 1841-1875* (Cardiff, 1958), p.50 et seq.
2   A.H.Dodd, *The Industrial Revolution in North Wales* (Cardiff, 2nd. ed., 1951), p.202.
3   A.R. Griffin, *Coalmining* (London, 1971), p.7, and C.Wilkins, *The South Wales Coal Trade* (Cardiff, 1888), p.97.
4   W.G.Thomas, *Welsh Coal Mines* (Cardiff, 1986), pp.125-6.
5   Griffin, *Coalmining*, pp.125-6.
6   Griffin, *Coalmining*, p.83 et seq.
7   C.M.Percy, *The Mechanical Equipment of Collieries* (Manchester, 1905), pp.243-257.
8   The Colliery Guardian, CXVI, G74 (26 July 1918), p.173.
9   Morris and Williams, *South Wales Coal Industry*, p.69.
10 J.Davey, *Mining Coal* (1976), p.83 et seq.
11 W.S.Boulton (ed.), *Practical Coal Mining* (Cardiff, 1907), vol. 2, p.256.
12 N.C.B. Production Department, Spoil Tip Management (1968).

Two miners work at the end of a heading. Despite extensive mechanization, there are still numerous uses for the compressed air hand-held drill, for making shot-blasting holes, rock trimming and roof-bolting.

Although superseded for illumination by the helmet-mounted battery light, the traditional miners' safety lamp has been adapted and improved and finds a use in the modern colliery to give a visual indication of the presence of gas, complementing the electronic air monitors in widespread use. (British Coal)

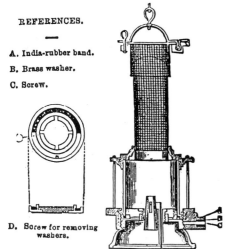
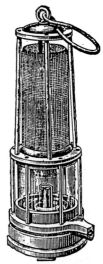
Advertisments for safety lamps, 1886 and 1900; E.Thomas had evidently merged with Williams between these dates.
The Clanny lamp, dating from 1811, was generally considered safer than the Davy lamp and was in use until about 1900.
('The Colliery Guardian')

*Workmen inspecting Forge Level or River Arch, Big Pit, in 1982. This view shows a contemporary method of roof support -
the continuous brick arch - for a permanent drainage adit built in the 1830s.*

Big Pit underground engine house with arched roof. It is thought that this engine house, probably dating from the mid-nineteenth century, enclosed a beam winding-engine which was used for underground haulage.

(Above): Engine Pit Level at Big Pit; a flywheel from an old haulage engine was used to build the roadside packs Note the ad hoc arrangement of timber and stone support for the roof.
(Right): Drawing of 50 & 60 horse-power electric double-drum haulage.
(British Coal drawing, National Library of Wales)

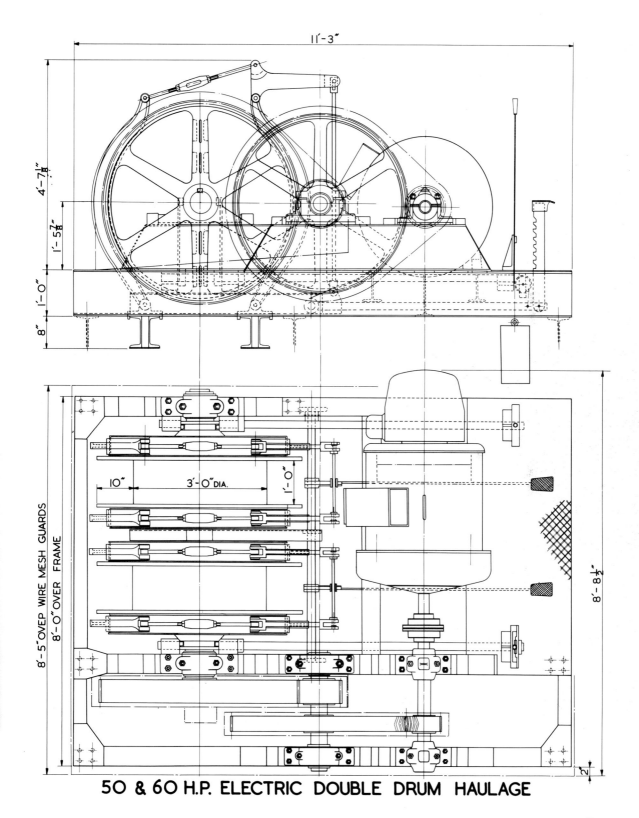

50 & 60 H.P. ELECTRIC DOUBLE DRUM HAULAGE

11'-3"

4'-7⅛"

1'-5⅝"

1'-0"

8"

8'-5" OVEP WIRE MESH GUARDS

8'-0" OVER FRAME

10"

3'-0" DIA.

1'-0"

8'-8½"

2"

(Above): Bottom of downcast shaft, 1978. In the 1950s Abertillery New Mine was opened using the shafts of Rose Heyworth Colliery, and coal from Cwmtillery and Blaenserchan was wound through it. As there was insufficient clearance at the sides of the shaft bottom, hinged steps were used to allow access to the upper deck of the cage; these were hoisted out of the way when not required to allow rail trams to pass.

(Opposite, top): Reproduction of advertisement from 'The Colliery Guardian', 23 Sept.1892.

(Opposite, below): The Tredomen engineering works at Hengoed produced machines for the Powell Duffryn Company and then the whole of the south Wales coalfield after nationalization. This is their underground haulage-engine design of 1977.

(Above): View of an active coalface in 1976 (Celynen South Colliery), showing the conveyor, roof supports and a ranging drum shearer in operation. The cutter can be raised and lowered in order to cut closely to the extremities of the seam; a modern development is the 'nucleonic' shearer which senses the proximity of the rock floor or roof and steers itself up or down accordingly.

(Opposite): Reproduction of an advertisement for an electric coal-cutter for longwall mining, from 'The Colliery Guardian', 1900. Early cutting machines such as this were unreliable, produced copious amounts of lethal coal dust before water suppression was applied in the late 1940s, and were not popular with the miners, being seen as a threat to the traditional labour intensive ways of getting coal by hand-tools.

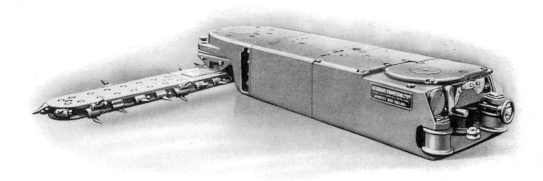

(Above): Man-riding conveyor belt (Marine Colliery). A great boon in easing the lot of the miner when travelling between shaft-bottom and workplace. Note the rope-worked supply railroad, and one of the rollers to guide the haulage rope and prevent it from dragging along the sleepers. Several alternative transport methods have been employed underground, including the ground-level monorail, suspended monorail (Becorit system) and latterly FSVs or free-steered vehicles. The pipe above the miners carries compressed air. (British Coal)

(Opposite): Looking along a typical modern longwall coalface, 1982 (Lady Windsor Colliery). In this view on the right is the coal seam awaiting the next pass of the shearer, which will load coal onto the armoured-face scraper-chain conveyor (centre) for transport to the coal-winding shaft. The shearer drives itself along the toothed rack, visible on the left. A series of interconnected hydraulic supports hold up the roof and when the shearer has passed, the flexible conveyor is slewed over to the newly exposed face, the roof supports retract slightly in turn, pull themselves forward to cover the conveyor and await the next pass of the shearer. The roof then collapses behind the supports as the machinery moves towards the receding coalface. (British Coal)

(Above): Trunk roadway and junction when newly constructed at Cynheidre Colliery; note the high standard of roof support and railway trackwork, and the spacious impression of the gallery. There is usually no bracing at ground level, the lower ends of the supports resting on wooden 'foot blocks', each measuring about 9in. x 6in. x 4in. (225 x 150 x 100mm).
(Opposite): Reproduction of advertisements from 'The Colliery Guardian', 2 Feb.1900.

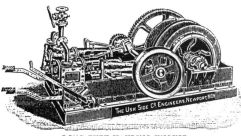

Colliery Headframes

Perhaps the most readily identifiable symbol of the coal industry is the distinctive outline of the colliery headframe, an adjunct to the winding process, its strength, size and material of construction reflecting both the ever increasing depth of shafts and power of the adjacent winding-engines.

Early shallow pits had their windlasses and capstans sited low over the pithead with no room for the manoeuvring of fleets of railway 'trams' or 'drams' and equipment. The only survivals from this period are the squat cast-iron frames from the Brynpwllog or Rogers Pit water balance, Rhymney, now at Big Pit, and other dismantled remnants of low cast-iron and wooden composite frames at Big Pit and at Cwmbyrgwm Water Pit, Abersychan. Some collieries had two high masonry walls supporting their winding sheaves as can be seen at Crimea Pit (1854) in the upper Swansea Valley. By the end of the nineteenth century the headframe 'sheaves' (pulley-wheels) were placed some 60ft. (18.3m.) above the shaft head. At least 30ft. (9.1m.) of clearance was needed for functional reasons. The tub or 'dram'- circuit, at the pithead or heapstead, often required an elevation of some 20ft. (6.1m.) to facilitate loading of main-line railway wagons at a lower level. Another 10ft. (3.05m.) was needed near the top of the headframe to accommodate the emergency detaching mechanisms introduced to prevent over-wound lift cages being crushed against the summit headframe sheave. As a result a height of 70ft. (21.3m.) was not unusual for large colliery head-frames in the early twentieth century. This was the height shown on the original colliery design drawings used in the construction of Britannia Colliery by the Powell Duffryn Steam Coal Company Limited.[1] Later the greater height of the headgear was often dictated by the use of multi-deck cages or large skips filled with coal. The depth of shaft and payload would dictate the sheave diameter and thus the size of the headgear platform. The width and breadth of the

The great depth of colliery shafts and the height of the cages meant that very strong headframes had to be constructed over the shafts. Illustrated is the headframe of Merthyr Vale Colliery with legs of bull-head rails bound by wrought-iron.

headframe tower was obviously determined by the necessity to give firm foundations clear of the shaft and also so as not to crowd the pit top. The distance between the centres of the two winding-ropes also determined the width of the headframe. Two main legs of the frame normally directly supported the winding-pulley, with diagonal braces to these vertical supports from the backstays. Some engineers aligned the backstay struts to bisect the lines of the under-rope and over-rope leading back to the winding-drum but this could sometimes lead to very long and shallow supports with several cross-braces. These distinctive backstays needed very secure foundations and, where possible, were often attached to the structure of the winding-engine houses (as, for example, at Abercynon, Deep Navigation and Marine Collieries).

Such was the length of the backstays at Deep Navigation (1872) that elegant arched trusses were also necessitated, extending from the backstays to the main vertical legs of the headframe. The lattice head-frames built by the Lewis Merthyr Navigation Colliery Limited (1878-90) were rather similar but have plainer diagonal struts supporting the backstays, as did Abercynon, Lady Windsor and Six Bells Collieries. Other engineers used much steeper backstays, resulting from the use of the principle of the parallelogram of forces, in which the angles of the backstays were determined by the bisection of the pull exerted diagonally by the winding-engine and that of the total vertical load of the winding-rope.[2] There were many differences in the theories of the determination of the correct angle and variations in actual construction.

In the early years of the twentieth century a majority of colliery headframes were still made of timber. The life of these was estimated as anything up to thirty years. The last of these pitch-pine frames went out of use in south Wales in 1964. The first wrought-iron lattice headframes were built in the mid-nineteenth century. Each of the many colliery companies had their own distinctive house-style. Some of the most distinctive were those built by the innovative owner, John Nixon. Merthyr Vale Colliery (1869-73), at Aberfan, had tapering headframes built of sections of wrought-iron bull-head rail bound together at intervals by wrought-iron bands riveted to the rail flanges, the frames being braced originally by cables rather than the more orthodox diagonal struts or backstays that were later added there. Many headframes like these, and including most twentieth-century examples, had four main legs of equal section. However, Edwardian colliery design manuals, and Victorian and Edwardian headframes as built, often recognized that there were 'two main legs' of crucial importance to the support of the winding-sheaves. This design rule was clearly used in the headframe of Nixon's Deep Duffryn Colliery at Mountain Ash (1888), which used two taller bull-head rail pillars to support the winding-sheaves directly. Both these structures were made at Nixon's Navigation Colliery foundry and workshops. The elegant headgear structures of Harris's Navigation Pits at Deep Navigation Colliery (1872) also had stouter main legs in the form of steel plate girders while the two subsidiary supports and backstays were made of lighter lattice-girder section. The logic of the structures was rarely followed through, as it was the smaller headframe at Tirpentwys which had no subsidiary backstays but only two main legs (main-stays) and two raking backstays.

By the end of the nineteenth century wrought-iron and steel joists were already beginning to replace lattice-girder towers. The earliest remaining is probably contemporary with the Hetty Shaft winding-engine house built at the Great Western Colliery in the Rhondda in 1875. It was the extremely long, narrow site that meant the backstays for these headframes rose at very steep angles because of the limited space available between engine house and headgear. Twin headframes of rolled steel in more conventional form also survive at Penallta (1906-08).

A reinforced-concrete headframes remains in use at Point of Ayr Colliery. This has main legs more widely raked towards resisting the thrust from the winder, so obviating the need for backstays.

One of the shafts at each colliery had to be the upcast shaft, with an airtight casing ensuring that the ventilation fan worked effectively. In many cases steel cladding gave the headframe tower itself an airtight seal.

All the pre-nationalization British coalfields remained faithful to the drum-winding of twin cages in the shaft on separate cables. The distinctive tall German headgear, with winding-pulleys placed above rather than alongside each other, was necessitated by the use of the Koepe system of winding in which a single driving pulley drove a continuous winding-rope with two cages attached. The driving-pulley was either positioned on the headgear, or on the ground, and the two vertical drops of the winding-rope were positioned by the two superimposed pulleys on the headgear. The lightness of the driving-pulley compared with a drum-winder meant that the power required for the operation was kept to a minimum. However, the possible savings accruing from the introduction of this new winding system were one of many innovations hardly applied to the relatively fragmented and under-capitalized pre-1947 British coalfields, and not used at all in the pre-nationalization coalfields of Wales. The distinctive headgear of vertically stacked driving-pulleys at Tirpentwys Colliery (Gwent) was similar to that used by the Koepe system, but with heavy double backstays leading back to a tall engine house housing a narrow winding-drum of conventional type. Exceptionally, only Tirpentwys and Hetty had winding-ropes that wrapped back upon themselves on narrow drums; the latter being a conversion from two flat-rope reels.

Of non-traditional type were the enclosed headframes of the collieries built in the 1950s at Abernant and Cynheidre which were capped by large cantilevered structures housing electrically-powered friction winders which were on the Koepe system. The latter also had a Koepe system headgear with the winding-engine situated alongside the frame at ground level. These have now been demolished and what remains in Wales is a selection of late-nineteenth- and early-twentieth-century metal headframes with the exception of the concrete headframe at Point of Ayr Colliery.

References

1. Glamorgan Archives Services, design drawing of Brittania Colliery headgear in British Coal collection.
2. C.M. Percy, *The Mechanical Equipment of Collieries* (Manchester, 1905), p.518.

Early headgears had a wonderful diversity of form with their sheaves (pulley-wheels) arranged in a variety of ways. By the second half of the twentieth century most headframes were capped by two sheaves alongside each other. An exception was Tirpentwys where the sheaves were arranged vertically on a frame with steeply inclined backstays leading to a tall engine-house that once housed a vertical steam winder. It also had one of the few narrow drums to survive on the coalfield into the later twentieth-century.

The length of the long inclined backstays on the fine lattice-girder headframes at Abercynon (1889) had themselves to be supported by intermediate struts. One of the two headframes at each pit, as here at Abercynon, capped a shaft that had used air drawn through it continuously by ventilation fans. It therefore had steel cladding to the headframe capping an airtight pithead building with double doors. Pictured opposite is the design drawing for the airtight casing over the north shaft of Britannia Colliery 1910-14. (British Coal Drawings, Glamorgan Archives Service)

- 7'-0" -

P.11 14'-8"

Outside of Sheeting 14'-1"

5'-0"   8'-0"   3'-2"

Y   X   X   Y   X

5'-0"   4'-0"

5'-0"   4'-0"

8'-0"

5'-0"

Horizontal L° on
Purlins 3½·3½·¼

8'-0"

3/16" Steel Plate   3/16" Steel Plate

4'-2" Centres

E   F   2½·2½·¼ L.   5½·5½·¾ L°

5'-2" Centres

Two 1"dia holes to be drilled
in each length of plate for
connecting to Pit head frame
except in bottom plate where one
will do.

12½·3½ Channel

3·3·⅜ L

C.I. Washer

14½·6 R.S.J.

- Section at E.F. -

14'·4" Centres

Top of Brickwork

9'-0"   22'-6"

Groove in Brickwork
to make air tight joint
with sheeting
- Section A.B. -

16'-3" Opening

12'-0"
EXTENSION

23'-6" Opening

23'-6" Opening   4'-3" Opening

2/6
Haslet
Splay

N° angle necessary at base
of splay.   - Front View -

25'-0"

28'-10"

Channel 12½·35

4'-6" R.S.J.

3½·3½·⅜ Angle

Outside of Sheeting 28'-10" at Base   Outside of Sheeting 14'-10"

4'-0"

14'-0"

Centre Line of Opening   Centre Line of Pit

9-1½dia holes
for 1½" D. bolts

- PROPOSED MILD...

-UPCAS... PI...

-P.D.S...

- SPECIFICATION. -

The casing to be composed of Mild Steel Plate 3/16" thick. The vertical corner angles to be 3" x 3" x 3/8". All horizontal angles & also vertical angles of partition to be $3\frac{1}{2}$" x $3\frac{1}{2}$" x 3/8".

The partition to be 3/16" thick & to extend from the top to a point 14'-0" from the base. Window openings to be formed where shown & stiffened all around by $2\frac{1}{2}$" x $2\frac{1}{2}$" x 3/8" angles, a margin of 2" to be left from angle to edge of opening as shown on plan. 6 - 5/8" dia holes to be drilled round each window opening where shown on plan. An opening to be left in front & back of casing as shown 23'-6" x 16'-3".

No angle connection to extend further than 3" from the edge of this opening as the plate will enter a groove in the brickwork (as shown in detail) to form air tight joint. The four corners at the base of casing to be splayed as shown to clear the base plates of Pit Head Frame. A 4" x 4" x $\frac{1}{2}$" angle to be securely rivetted to base of bottom side plate & to have 9 - $1\frac{1}{4}$" dia holes for $1\frac{1}{8}$" dia x 12" long Lewis bolts. The 12" x 6" R.S.J. X & Y to be supplied by the contractor. The R.S.J. Y to be joggled into R.S.J. X & to have the standard cleat connection. The 3/16" Top plate of casing to be connected to the bottom flanges of the R.S.Js X & Y. Two openings to be formed in the top, between R.S.Js X each to be 14'-6" x 5'-2". The holes for connecting R.S.Js X to existing girder G will be drilled by P.D.Cº on the site.

The Casing to be constructed so that every
~~joint~~ will be perfectly Air tight.
The whole of the work to be completed and
~~in~~ every respect to be thoroughly made in every
~~detail~~ of the best workmanship & material.
The foregoing Specification & drawing
~~to~~ be adhered to as far as possible, but no error or
~~omission~~ or other cause whatsoever, shall relieve
~~the~~ makers of entire responsibility for the efficiency
~~of~~ the work in every detail when completed & erected.

Price to include delivery (<u>but not erection</u>)
~~Carriage~~ paid onto the site at:-
Britannia Colliery
Pengam Station
Brecon & Merthyr Railway.

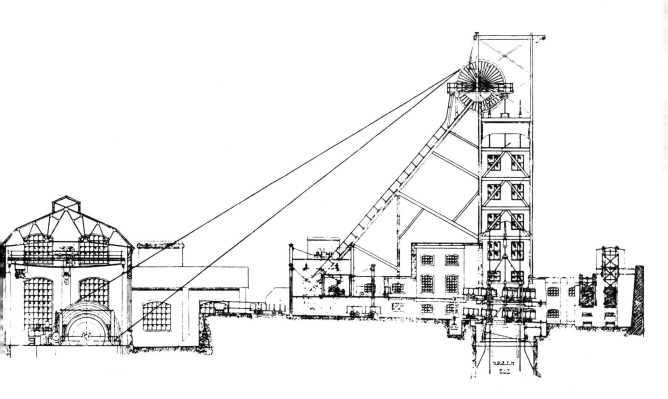

Detailed written specifications survive for the airtight cladding erected at Britannia Colliery in 1910-14, and accompanied the design drawing pictured on the previous page. The cross-section drawing on this page also shows the reinforced-concrete airtight building at the head of the North Pit and the relationship of the headframe to the winding-drum in the common engine-hall alongside. (Specification with British Coal drawings, Glamorgan Archives Service and cross-section from 'The Colliery Guardian', 1918)

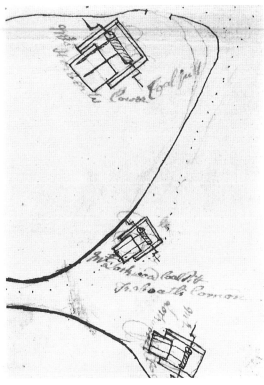

(Left): The shallow coal-pits found in profusion on Treboeth Common, Swansea, in the early eighteenth century had simple well-like windlasses set on small timber frames above them. (National Library of Wales, Badminton Collection, Group II, 1454)

(Opposite page): The fine lattice-girder headframe at Lady Windsor Colliery was made in Glamorgan by the Cardiff Junction Drydock & Engineering Company Limited in 1886.

(Below): The winding-towers built at Cynheidre (seen here) and Abernant Collieries in the 1950s were of a radically different design from earlier headframes and supported tower-top winders driving narrow Koepe-system sheaves rather than the earlier large winding-drums. (British Coal)

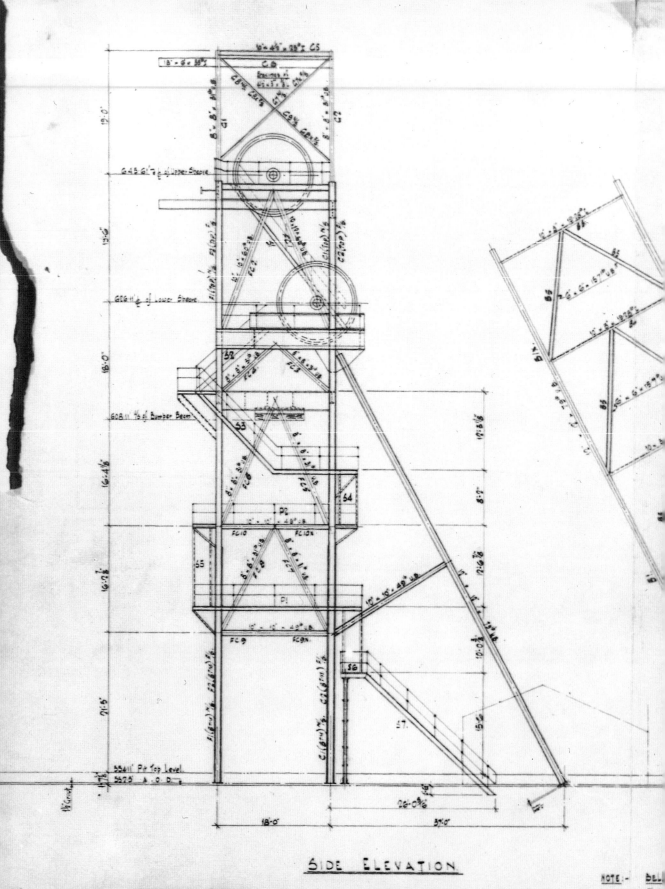

SIDE ELEVATION

On Admiralty and Lloyd's Lists for Steel Castings

BROWN, LENOX & CO. LTD., PONTYPRIDD.

ALL STEEL CASTINGS from "Electric" Furnace.

Castings made to any Specification

Reproduction of an advertisement from 'The Colliery Guardian', 1900, showing a variety of Glamorgan-made sheaves and pulley-wheels.

(Opposite page): The design drawing for the only Koepe headframe at Cynheidre (1954-56) to use a ground-based winder. The Koepe system of continuous winding used a powered sheave and the stacked arrangement of the headframe sheaves in the drawing reflects the use of the system. (British Coal drawings, National Monuments Record of Wales)

Winding Coal

Good winding equipment is the key to any deep mine as it is responsible for conveying men and every single item of material and machinery into and out of the pit. The engine provides motive power for the drum around which is wound a cable attached to containers travelling in the shafts.

The earliest form of winding was by simple windlass, or *jack-roll*, powered by manual labour. These were the only mechanical devices used in early mines and were perfectly adequate for the simple shallow workings of the later medieval period. Use of shafts at this time was limited to raising baskets or buckets of coal to the surface. The windlass was recorded in common use all over Wales by the seventeenth century. George Owen, writing in the first decade of the seventeenth century, described how Pembrokeshire colliers *'sink their pits down right four square about six or seven feet square, and with a windlass turned by four men they draw up the coals by rope, a barrelful at once.'* A typical pit might have sixteen workers, three of whom were miners hewing the coal with pickaxes, and 80 to 100 barrels a day were raised up the shaft. At the opposite north-eastern corner of Wales, around Holywell in Flintshire, it was similarly said by Celia Fiennes in 1698 that the miners *'draw up their coale in sort of baskets like hand barrows which they wind up like a bucket in a well'*. Treboeth Common, at Swansea, in the early eighteenth century was dotted with such coal-winding windlasses. 'Windlass women' were commonly employed in Pembrokeshire drawing baskets of coal up and down to the main mining tunnels.[1]

In the latter part of the seventeenth century, as mining activity began to intensify, early forms of horse-engine or *gin* developed and were used for raising coal and water. One type was the *cog and rung* gin, effectively the manual windlass on a larger scale but adapted for horse operation. The animal walked round the pit top attached to a short beam fixed to a vertical axle upon which a horizontal crown-wheel was mounted; cogs in the wheel engaged a small pinion on the windlass, so turning it in the required direction.[2]

This method of lifting soon showed its limitations and was improved by moving the mechanism a short distance from the mouth of the shaft. Ropes were run from the windlass drum to pulleys mounted in a timber frame built over the shaft. This *whim-gin* was a much better arrangement as the top of the shaft was clear of obstruction, there was more room for the diameter of the winding-drum to be increased, and the number of horses required to wind could be adjusted as necessary. Such an installation was depicted at Treboeth Colliery in the Swansea Valley in an elaborate structural form with a circular enclosing wall pierced by the entrances to three service buildings.

In one large colliery a gin was recorded in which eight horses were used to raise the coal. The team of horses was kept at a sharp trot, and a large horizontal wheel used to give greater speed to the drum; even so the machine could raise a load of only 6cwt.(305kg.) of coal from a depth of 100 fathoms (183m.) in two minutes.[3]

Numerous schemes were devised to use water power for bringing coal to the surface. In 1753, at Chatershaugh Colliery on the River Wear in north-eastern England, Michael Menzies used a simple balancing system whereby the descent of a bucket of water raised a lighter basket of coal. It was capable of drawing 5cwt (278kg.) of coal from a depth of 50 fathoms (92m.) in two minutes. This water-balance or *balance-tub* method became common in south Wales during the first half of the nineteenth century and by the mid-century there were over sixty such balances working in Glamorgan alone. The majority of these

(Opposite): Small shaft winding steam-winch set in the foundation of one of the two main winding-engines at Marine Colliery.

(Overleaf): Plans of the circular walled horse-walk constructed in 1758 alongside Llangyfelach Road in Swansea to wind from Treboeth Colliery , with drawings of the five colliers' houses which were to be constructed in 1768. (National Library of Wales, Badminton Collection, Group II, 1282 & 1283,)

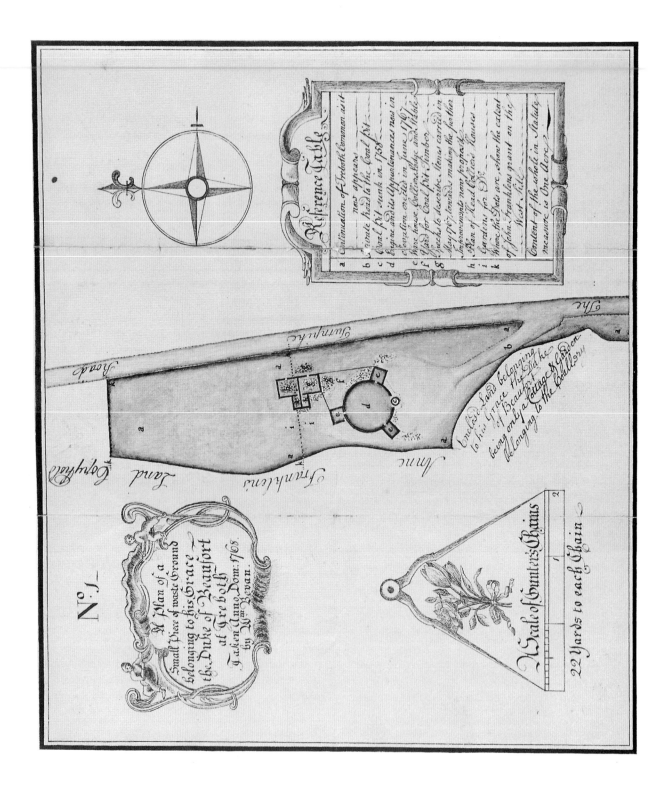

No. 1.

A Plan of a
Small Peice of waste Ground
belonging to his Grace
the Duke of Beaufort
at Treboth
Taken Anno Dom: 1768.
by Wm. Bevan.

Reference Table

a   Continuation of Treboth Common as it
        next appears
b   Seperate head to the Coal pit
c   Coal pit sunk in 1768
d   Engine and its Appurtenances now in
        elevation erected in June 1767
e   Shops house Outbuildings and Stable
F   Yard for Coal pit Timber
g   Tracks to describe Stones carried in
        May 1767 Franklin making the justice
h   Improvements now proposed
i   Plan of Head Colliers Kennel
k   Gardens for Do
l   Where the Spots are show the extent
        of John Franklins grant on this
        West hill
    Content of the whole in Statute
        measure to One Acre

Scale of Gunters Chains

22 Yards to each Chain

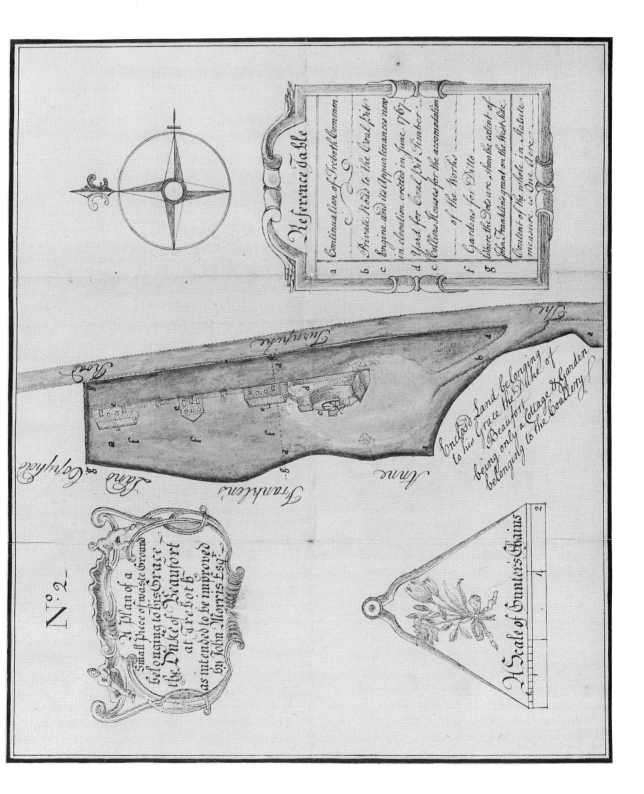

were confined to outcrop workings where the shafts were comparatively shallow and where there was a plentiful supply of water. Used water was run off through a drainage adit underground. A major drawback was that winding was curtailed during periods of drought, although of course upland Wales was rarely short of water, and contemporary observers between 1800 and 1850 suggest that the use of the water-balance was then peculiar to the south Wales coalfield.[4]

A detailed description survives of a variant of nineteenth-century water-balance winding at Ynys Merthyr Colliery, in the Swansea Valley, where water was raised to the surface by means of a waterwheel. The winding-gear consisted of a trestle headframe, about 20ft. (6.1m.) in height, carrying a large pulley around which a chain was passed suspending a cage at each end.[5] A dam was constructed at the mouth of the lower adit, which served as a storage reservoir. Water was conveyed through a 6in. (0.15m.) cast-iron pipe to a tank connected to a valve box set in the middle of the shaft so arranged as to fill the tanks under the cages.[6] Several variations of the water-balance were used and remained the most efficient method of winding coal from deep pits until the development of suitable steam-winders.

The earliest heavy investment in the development of the south Wales coalfield took place where it was first accessible to cheap bulk transport, i.e. along the coast from Llanelli to Neath. Here, in the early eighteenth century, wealthy merchants and industrialists built substantial water leats, sometimes of considerable length, in order to work water-powered beam-engines draining colliery shafts along their routes. Reversible double waterwheels had been known in the German mining areas of Europe since the sixteenth century, and local engineers such as 'Mr. Powell' of Morriston erected their own variants, here described in 1783 with reference to Landore Coalpit near Swansea:

'...he has erected Several Engines with great improvements - and invented a very simple but consequential contrivance to draw the Coal from a Pitt about 100 yds. [91m.] from an Engine, the Water from thence being carried to a Water Wheel, which being made double close together only revers'd receives the water first on One which draws up, then is diverted to the other that turns it the other way and lets down, the rope being round the Shaft and runs on each side alternately as the Wheel reverses - One Man only attends the pitt, shifts the Stream, receives the Coal, empties and returns the baskets - and with such expedition that it draws 150 Tons of Coal in 24 Hours.'[7]

Simple steam-pumps such as Thomas Savery's had been used in coalmines since the seventeenth century, and 'Mr Powell' had also obviously developed a variant of this, or an early hydraulic ram to aid water-wheel-winding during drought:

'close to this is a small but curious Engine to throw the Water when it is scarce and they are short of it - They tell me it is of singular simple Construction, his own Invention and without some Customary Movements, but I do not know enough of the Matter to describe it.'

Steam power was not quickly adapted from its widespread use for pumping to the task of direct winding. Early steam-engines had only single-acting pistons so could not easily produce the required rotative motion needed for winding. Despite early experiments in south Wales and elsewhere in applying steam to winding, sources of water power were readily available in a land of heavy rainfall and hilly terrain, and carried-on in use.

Towards the end of the eighteenth century, James Watt developed the rotary motion double-acting engine that could be applied directly to a winding-drum shaft. However in 1783 George Watson, a representative of Boulton & Watt, visited John Morris, managing director of the copper-smelting and coalmining concern of Lockwood, Morris & Co. at Landore, Swansea, and 'found him in deep affliction and real distress, having that day by a most melancholy and unfortunate accident lost Mr. Powell his Engineer who being down repairing the Engine, by accident the plug of the Steampipe dropt out, when the Steam issued with such force as to scald him so dreadfully that he died in two days, - most Universally lamented, - It seem this man was a wonderful prodigy of nature, a person who had achieved such extraord[inar]y feats ... He came there about 20 years ago a young man and common blacksmith, who from working for and attending on the millwrights and engineers, was so expert and clever, that he had only to perceive to *comprehend, and from comprehending to execute, insomuch that he undertook to construct an Engine, which he effected far superior to any before, made everything himself - and it went to work the very first day with ease, expedition and regularity and so continued without alteration, from which time he has erected Several Engines with great improvements.'*

In fact, some time between 1763 and 1783, Mr. Powell had built rotary atmospheric steam-engines to wind coal on the lower western side of the Swansea Valley between Landore and Morriston.[8] Interestingly, the long low shape of a surviving engine house at Gwernllwynchwith, a short distance south of the tall and short Scott's Pit pumping-engine house, indicates its origin as a winding-engine house. This building, now an ivy-covered ruin, was built between 1772 and 1782 but was out of use by 1786.[9] It is commonly supposed that no rotary steam-engines were used before Watt's improved engine, which was first applied to coal-winding in 1784. The first Watt winder in Glamorgan was at Plas-y-Marl, Swansea, in 1787, but seven years later there were still only two at work in the collieries of the county.[10]

With the expiry of Watt's Patent in 1800, the way was open for condensing rotary steam-engines to be freely manufactured locally, and most of the large works did this. Richard Trevithick was also in Glamorgan at Penydarren, Aberdare and Abernant in 1803-04 negotiating licences for the manufacture of his small high-pressure non-condensing machines which were admirably suitable for the replacement of existing waterwheel-winders. Alexander Raby's Trevithick-designed 'Engine Fach' was installed near Cilfig on the Llanelli Coalfield in 1804. This was a 4-6 h.p. engine, with 7in. (0.15m.) cylinders, operating at 25 p.s.i. (1.75kg/cm^2.) but capable of being operated at 50 p.s.i. (3.5kg/cm^2.)[11] In the previous year such a machine had been installed alongside the huge Boulton and Watt pump at Landore, Swansea, on the coalpit of the copper magnate, John Morris. This had 8in. (0.2m) cylinders working at 40-48 p.s.i. (2.8-3.4 kg/cm^2).[12] These small machines would have been almost identical to Trevithick's 1804 Penydarren Tramroad locomotive minus powered wheels.

Interestingly it was common in the early nineteenth century to have one large steam-engine for both pumping and winding. In the survey of colliery steam-engines carried out in the Swansea and Neath Valleys in about *ca*.1840 it was recorded that ten of the fifteen steam-winders then in use were of this type (including one old-fashioned atmospheric engine). Indeed the two winders that survive from the mid-nineteenth century (at Glyn Pits, Pontypool and Pontypridd (ex. Newbridge Colliery)) are both combined pumping and winding-engines, as are many of the engines shown on the Neath Abbey Ironworks drawings.[13]

The deeper pits of the mid-nineteenth century all required more powerful machines than the tiny Trevithick engines built in 1803-4. By about *ca*.1840 two of the five winders in use around Swansea and Neath were high-pressure engines. One then in use was twice as powerful as the early engines being of 12 h.p. with 12in. (0.3m.) cylinders and a 3ft. stroke. Another, being erected at Cwmbela Pit, was four times as powerful as the early machines, having 24in. (0.61m.) diameter cylinders and a 3ft. (0.91m.) stroke. Other specialist winding machines were low-pressure engines ranging from the 32in. (0.81m.) cylinder winder with its 6ft. (1.83m.) stroke at Church Pit, Llansamlet; through the 24in. (0.61m.) 20 h.p. engine at Neath Abbey Colliery with its 5ft. (1.52m.) stroke, to the 13in. (0.33m.) winder at Scott's Pit, Llansamlet with a stroke of 5 ft.(1.52m.) (whose footings can still be seen).[14]

The first steam-winding engine in the famous Rhondda Valleys was at Newbridge Colliery; built by the Varteg Iron works, near Abersychan, in 1845, it was also used for pumping. Brown Lenox & Co. of Pontypridd supplied a replacement cylinder in 1861, and the engine operated until 1919. It now stands in the grounds of the University of Glamorgan at Treforest.[15]

The steam winding-engine seemed to have almost limitless power potential and enabled shafts to be sunk even deeper and greater quantities of coal to be raised with each wind.

In the eighteenth and early nineteenth centuries coal had been brought up the shafts in wicker baskets; as often were the workers. Each basket at the Llansamlet collieries in Swansea held between 6 and 8 cwt. (305-407 kilos) of coal. They were transported underground on trolleys running on tramroad rails.[16] In December 1834 at South Hetton Colliery, in the huge Durham

Coalfield, cages were used to raise trams of coal to the surface for the first time in Britain. At this particular colliery both surface and underground railways were used to convey trams to and from the shaft. The floors of the cages were fitted with short lengths of rail to connect with the railways, thus creating an efficient tram-handling system which quickly spread and is still in use at many collieries.

The considerable weight of the longer ropes coming into use as shafts became deeper was itself a great load on the winding-engine. In 1856 Henry Burrows devised a simple system using a tail rope suspended below the cages as a counterbalance.

Ordinary hemp ropes became increasingly unsuitable for working in deep shafts. Installing larger diameter ropes would have raised more problems with the greater size of winding-drum required. During 1835-6 iron-wire ropes were used in the collieries of Prussia, where they were found to be an economical solution - they could carry greatly increased loads and were used for much longer operating periods. Wire ropes were first used in Britain at St. Lawrence Colliery, Newcastle, and were soon common in Wales. The surviving flat wire-rope vertical winder at Glyn Pits dates from the period 1856-65. Vertical winding-engines, and inverted vertical engines (as at Deep Navigation) became quite common in south Wales during the third quarter of the nineteenth century.

Steam winding-engines were generally horizontally mounted by the fourth quarter of the nineteenth century. In a typical installation, a pair of engines was coupled directly to the drum shaft, one on each side of the drum, with their cranks offset so that both engines could never be on the dead-centre of a stroke simultaneously and hence unable to start. Connected to the crankshaft was an indicator which showed the position of the cages in the shaft to help guard against under- or, more seriously, over-winding. Alongside one of the engines was placed a lever for working the reversing gear, and another lever for working a valve used for regulating steam to the engine. There was also a foot pedal for working the brake on the drum.[17]

Winding-engines needed an enormous amount of power at the start of a wind to overcome inertia, and considerable braking force to stop. Early in the twentieth century they were frequently rated at 1,000 or 1,500 h.p. and could attain a cage speed of 96km/h. To help an engine start a wind the spiral or conical winding-drum was developed. It was already in use in 1787 when Boulton & Watt supplied one for Plas-y-Marl Colliery at Swansea, a second spiral controlling a counter-weight in the shaft. The rope lay round a small diameter part of the drum at the start of a wind, and as speed increased the rope wound up a shallow cone or spiral and onto the main cylindrical section. The minimum and maximum diameters of the drum were based on specific data, such as the available power, speed required, and weight of the ropes, cages, trams and coal. The more developed *bi-cylindro-conical drum* was recorded in use in the Lancashire coalfield in the middle of the nineteenth century. In south Wales John Nixon made his own development of the type at Deep Duffryn Colliery.[18] Examples of such drums survive at the East Elliot (Tredegar) and Trevor (Lewis Merthyr Colliery) engine houses. Later drums were fabricated from steel plates, and were consequently much lighter than the traditional cast-iron cylindrical drums so that the inertia to be overcome was then lessened both by their design and construction.[19]

While a modern winding-drum is rotating, it typically draws up one cage and lowers the other, requiring relatively little power input, and in fact acts as a flywheel giving smooth winding. The braking system serves two functions - to bring the drum to a halt, and to hold it steady once it has been brought to a stand. The brake, when off, does not present any mechanical drag to the drum and needs very little movement but considerable force to act. Steam brakes were widely installed and gave a powerful, reliable means of stopping several tons of rotating iron and steel, the effective control of which was vital to the safety of miners travelling in the cages.

The winding-house was often the largest of the surface buildings at a colliery, accommodating the huge engines and winding-drums. By erecting one large engine house to take all the main machinery, the necessary room could be obtained at less capital cost than by constructing separate buildings, and was more convenient and efficient to operate. Such common

(Opposite): The control room for the electrically-powered winder at Maerdy Colliery (1947-53) with its brake visible encircling the winding-drum.

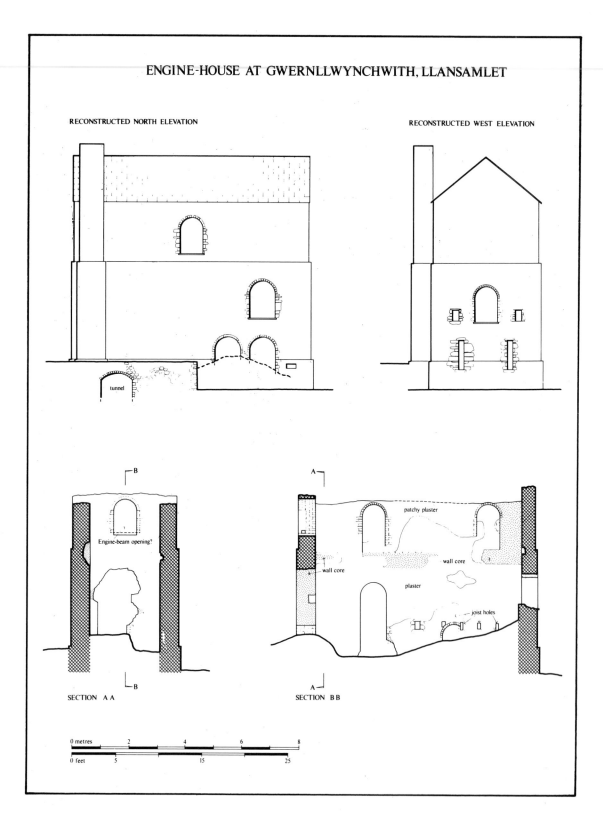

ENGINE-HOUSE AT GWERNLLWYNCHWITH, LLANSAMLET

RECONSTRUCTED NORTH ELEVATION

RECONSTRUCTED WEST ELEVATION

tunnel

B

A

Engine-beam opening?

patchy plaster

wall core

wall core

plaster

joist holes

SECTION A A

SECTION B B

0 metres   2   4   6   8

0 feet   5   15   25

engine-halls may have been devised by German engineers but in Britain were probably first used by the Powell Duffryn Company at Penallta and elsewhere. The length of the steam supply pipes was reduced to a minimum, labour and supervision were reduced and one powerful overhead crane could serve all the engines and machinery.[20] At most of the Welsh pits it remained normal practice to have separate buildings for the winding-engines, compressors and main ventilating fans. The first skip-winding collieries were equipped by German firms in the late 1930s. Skips are steel containers used exclusively for carrying coal up the shafts, and latterly the loading at pit bottom and discharge at the surface were semi- or fully automatic operations, with the skips awaiting loading, resting below the level of the bottom roadways. The engineering company, Qualter Hall negotiated to manufacture this equipment under licence and after 1945 skip-winding became widespread throughout Wales and England.[21]

For the building and equipping of Penallta Colliery, tenders were invited from some of the largest electrical and steam-engineering firms in the country. At this time the electric winding-engine could not compete with steam, either in capital cost or in economy of running. Capital cost of an electric winder, with the added expense of providing generators as there was no outside supply of electricity, amounted to nearly three times the cost of a four-cylinder compound engine, so it was decided to adopt steam winding-engines from Fraser & Chalmers. At No.1 pit a cross-compound Corliss valve engine was installed, having 28in and 46in (0.71m and 1.17m) diameter cylinders with a 60in (1.52m) stroke. It turned a cast-iron bi-cylindro-conical drum of 8ft to 12ft (2.44m to 3.66m) diameter. Although the engine was quite small, it was able to deal with a net load of nearly 9 tons from a depth of 711m.

At the No.2 pit another compound engine was used, with cylinders of 32in and 53in (0.81m and 1.35m) diameter and 6ft. (1.83m) stroke, driving a parallel drum 16ft (4.87m) in diameter. The engine was capable of winding two trams at a time a distance of

Steam winders were developed by the 1780s by local engineers such as 'Mr Powell' at Landore-Morriston; archaeological evidence for such a structure survives at Llansamlet , Swansea.

684m. in 45 seconds and of dealing with an output of 180 tons per hour.[22]

As colliery generating-plants became more efficient, it was soon clear that electricity would replace steam as the motive power for winding-engines. Old Duffryn and Abercwmboi Collieries had electric winders from 1906. The Britannia Colliery (Pengam) of 1910-14 was the first completely all-electric pit (in Wales and internationally). It accompanied the setting up of company-specific electrical grids, but more widespread electrification took place after nationalization of the coal industry in 1947 when the national grid was fully established. The period saw a massive colliery re-equipment programme, including the uprating and electrification of winding-engines throughout south Wales, and a number of show pits were developed.

Electric winders produce uniform torque, a distinct advantage over the pulsations of steam drive, giving smoother winding and causing less wear on ropes and shaft guides. The electric winder achieves a much higher power output, easily reaching 3,000 h.p., and often much faster winding speeds; control is much more sensitive and precise.

Nationalization also meant that ideas were gleaned for the operation of Welsh pits from all over Europe. Herr Koepe, an engineer for Krupp and Company in Germany, had developed a system which dispensed with the heavy colliery winding-drum some hundred years before the introduction of his system to south Wales. However, none of the relatively conservative British coalfields adopted this practice widely before nationalization. In the Koepe system ropes and cages formed a continuous loop suspended over a large deeply-grooved driving-pulley mounted in the head-frame. Apart from the weight of coal being raised, the whole system was in balance.[23] After nationalization the system was introduced in building new collieries: Cynheidre Colliery using a conventionally sited electric winder on the ground in 1954-56, but subsequent use at both Abernant (in 1958) and Cynheidre involved the use of tower-based winders. Large-scale shaft haulage in Wales was later somewhat displaced by the widespread use of new inclined tunnels ('slants' or 'drifts') as can still be seen at Betws, Tower and Point of Ayr Collieries.

References

1   A.H. John, *The Industrial Development of South Wales*, (Cardiff, 1950), p.147; W. Rees, *Industry before the Industrial Revolution* (Cardiff, 1968), vol.i, p.122; M. Bevan-Evans, *Early Industry in Flintshire*, (Hawarden, 1966), p.12; and National Library of Wales, Badminton Collection, Group II, 1282.

2   R.L. Galloway, *A History of Coal Mining in Great Britain* (London, 1882).

3   ibid., recording practice at Walker Colliery in the north of England.

4   A.H. John, Industrial Development of South Wales, p.144.

5   The Institute of Mining Engineers Transactions III (1891-92).

6   ibid.

7   G.Watson to M.Boulton, 4 Jan.1783, Birmingham Central Library, M.Boulton Papers, Box W.

8   ibid.

9   Stephen Hughes & Paul Reynolds, *A Guide to the Industrial Archaeology of the Swansea Region,* (Aberystwyth, 2nd. ed., 1989), p.6.

10   Birmingham Reference Library, Boulton & Watt Collection, portfolio 28; (ed.) *A.H. John and G. Williams Glamorgan County History, Volume V, Industrial Glamorgan,* (Cardiff, 1980).

11   M.V. Symons, *Coal-Mining in the Llanelli Area, Vol.I. 16th Century to 1829* (Llanelli,1929), p.317.

12   E.T. Svedenstierna, *Svedenstierna's Tour of Great Britain 1802-3. The Travel Diary of an Industrial Spy* (Newton Abbot, 1973), p.46; R.P. Roberts, 'History of Coalmining in Gower from 1700 to 1832' (University of Wales (Cardiff), M.A. thesis, 1953), quoting A. Titley, 'Richard Trevithick and the Winding Engine', *The Transactions of the Newcomen Society* X (1929-30), pp.55-68.

13   Swansea Museum (RISW), Morgan MSS, 'Statistical Table of Steam Power, Swansea', and M. Palmer and P. Neaverson, 'The Steam Engines at Glyn Pits Colliery, Pontypool: an Archaeological Investigation', *Industrial Archaeology Review* XIII.1 (Autumn 1990), pp.26-32. Combined winding-and pumping-engines were common on other coalfields in the early nineteenth century. See, for example I. Ayris, 'Elemore Colliery', *Industrial Archaeology Review*, IV. 1 (Winter 1979-80), pp.6-35, 15.

14   'Statistical Table of Steam Power, Swansea', op cit.

15   J. Cornwell, *The Great Western and Lewis Merthyr Collieries* (Cowbridge, 1983), p.8.

16   A. Jackson, *Notes on Coal-Mining in the Llansamlet Area* (Swansea, 1987), p.4.

17   R.L. Galloway, *A History of Coal Mining in Great Britain* (London,1882), p.260.

18   C. Wilkins, *The South Wales Coal Trade* (Cardiff,1888), p.99.

19   C.M. Percy, *The Mechanical Equipment of Collieries* (Manchester, 1905), p.544.

20   ibid.

21   'The Centenary of Qualter Hall ', *The Colliery Guardian* (1960), p.539.

22   Proceedings of the South Wales Institute of Engineers XXVII (1910 -11), p.50.

23   G.M. Bailes, *Modern Mining Practice* (Sheffield, n.d.), vol. v, pp.210-12.

(Opposite): The small light cages at Morlais Colliery were wound by a simple two-cylinder winding-engine built by Andrew Barclay of Kilmarnock in about 1905. Generally coalmines required stouter headframes and more powerful winding-engines than non-ferrous metal mines because they were using large tram-cages, and later skips, in their shafts rather than the smaller kibbles of higher value metal ores.

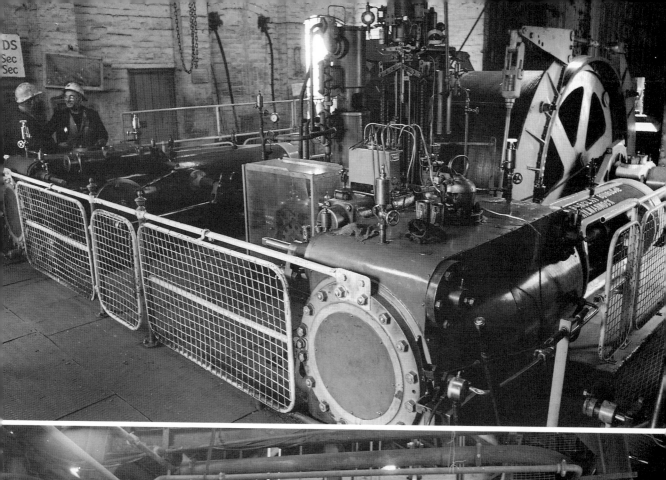

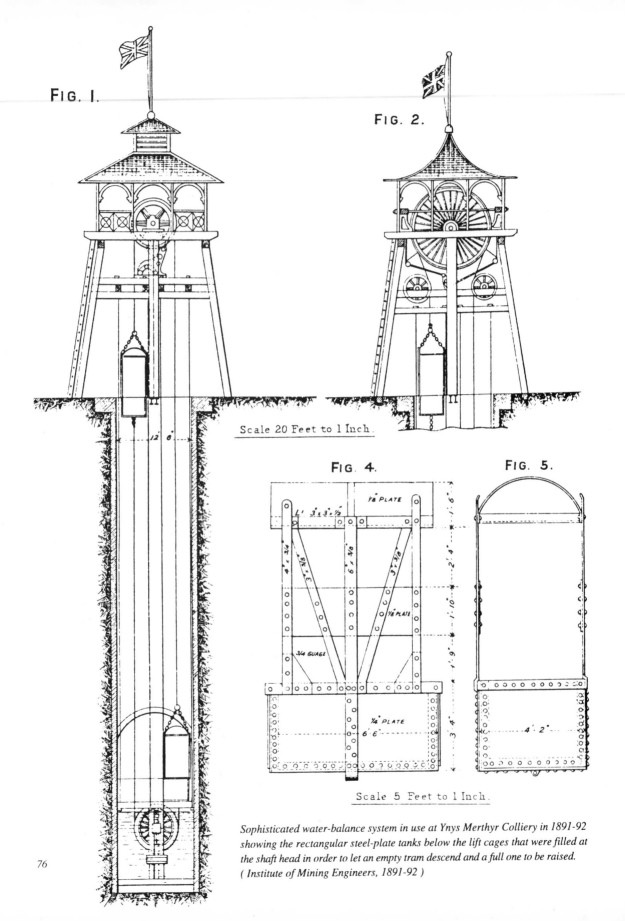

FIG. I.

FIG. 2.

Scale 20 Feet to 1 Inch.

FIG. 4.

⅛ PLATE

L' 3"x 3"x ½"

¼ PLATE

6' 6"

3/4 GUAGE

⅛ PLATE

1'-6"

2'-4"

1'-10"

1'-9"

3'-4"

FIG. 5.

4'-2"

Scale 5 Feet to 1 Inch.

*Sophisticated water-balance system in use at Ynys Merthyr Colliery in 1891-92
showing the rectangular steel-plate tanks below the lift cages that were filled at
the shaft head in order to let an empty tram descend and a full one to be raised.
(Institute of Mining Engineers, 1891-92)*

Water-balance winding became exceptionally common in the south Wales coalfield in the nineteenth century at a time when it had been abandoned in areas with lesser rainfall. This shaft at Cwmbyrgwm (before 1820), Abersychan, had very simple lift-cages. One cage still survives on site (pictured below). This had a circular wrought-iron plate watertank beneath its deck with a cast-iron cross-piece leading to the haulage chain above.

The fine masonry engine house and stack of the unique vertical steam-winder at Glyn Pits, Pontypool. In this side view of the engine house (built between 1856 and 1865) the axle end of the high winding-drum (the steam-engine is positioned beneath the drum) is visible at the base of the upper central opening. On the upper right wall one of the stone corbels and cast-iron shoes that formerly supported an inclined leg of the wooden headframe are visible.
(Redrawn from a survey by Cadw: Welsh Historic Monuments)

0   5   10 Metres

0   10   20   30 Feet

*The shafts-side wall of the winding engine house at Glyn Pits showing the three headframe supports on the upper-right elevation. The original intention may have been for the winding-cables to pass through the upper arched opening and also from at least the right-hand of the lower arched openings. By the end of the nineteenth century the engine was winding through two shafts simultaneously via two flat wire ropes (still in situ), powered by sheaves set on the high central axle, leading onto a tandem headframe with sheaves arranged over each of the two shafts. By the end of the century the ropes passed through the roof and through the crude slot cut above the right-hand of the arched openings.
(Redrawn from a survey by Cadw: Welsh Historic Monuments)*

This photograph shows the later nineteenth-century winding-engine house and chimney of the No.9 Pit of the Tredegar Iron & Coal Company. The Tredegar Company (reformed to sell more coal in 1873) was one of the main four old ironworks companies that had entered the coal sales market on a large scale.

(Opposite, below): Double beam-engine winder at Broadoak Colliery, Loughor. The original engine is that to the left.

(British Coal drawings, National Monuments Record of Wales)

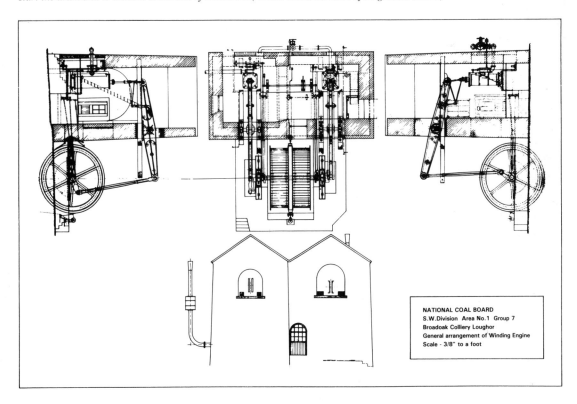

DETAIL of DRUM for Nº 1 WINDER.

(Above): The sheet-steel fabricated bi-cylindro-conical winding-drum, designed for Penallta Colliery in 1906-09, was lighter than previous cast-iron drums. The smaller diameter sections on the drum sides helped reduce the power needed both to start the drum and to brake it at the end of a descent. ('South Wales Institute of Engineers', 1910)

NATIONAL COAL BOARD
S.W.Division Area No.1 Group 7
Broadoak Colliery Loughor
General arrangement of Winding Engine
Scale - 3/8" to a foot

(Opposite): The use of skips (from 1945) in winding increased the haulage capacity in a shaft over that of the smaller trams (example on the surface at Lady Windsor Colliery).

(Below): The winding-engine house at the Hetty Shaft (1875) of the Great Western Colliery. As with many valleyside structures the engine house sits on a very tall podium with the steam winding-engine on the floor-level sited above the upper string-course. Beyond the engine house were open ranges of boilers and on the nearside of it is the fan-house with the steeply inclined back-stays of the headframe beyond.

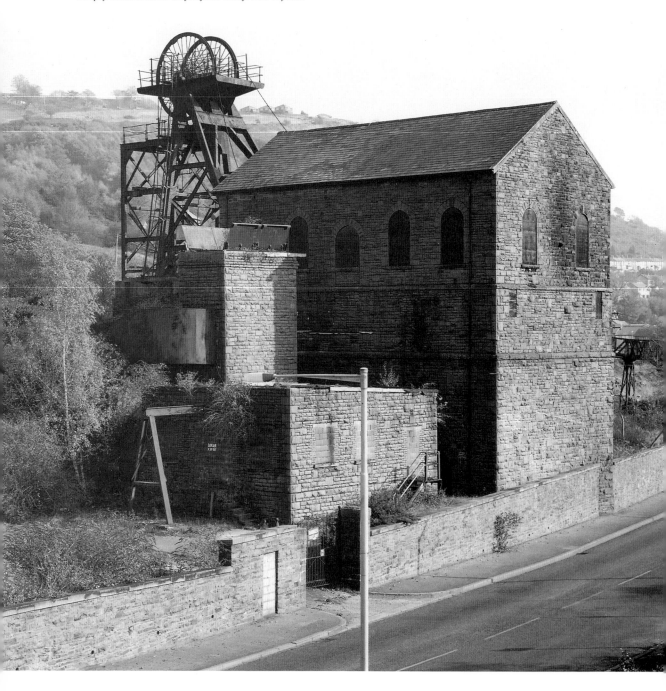

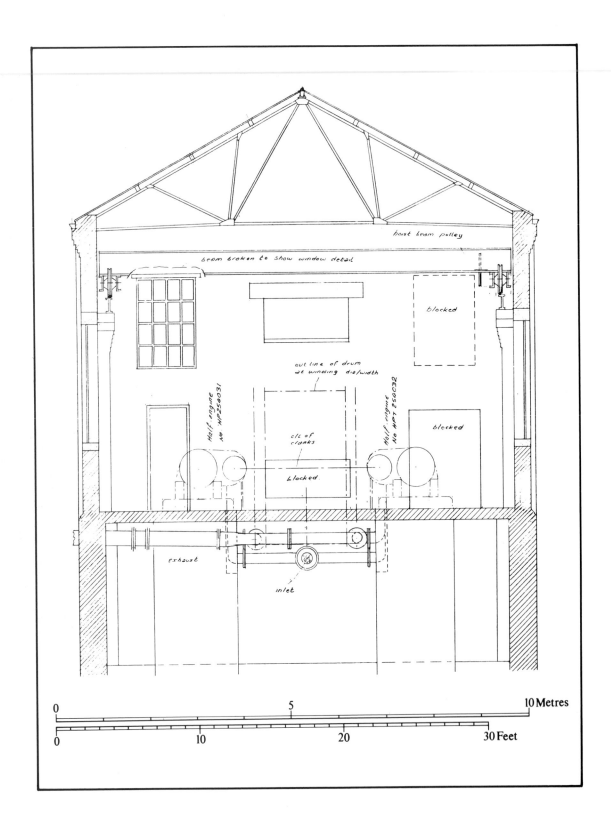

(Above): The two-cylinder winding-engine at the Point of Ayr Colliery with driving cranks attached to both sides of the winding-drum. The engine was made by Worsley Mesnes of Wigan in 1924 and was a 'simple' rather than a compound engine, using the steam only once. This engine has been removed for re-erection at the Bersham Heritage Centre near Wrexham, while a second engine made by the same manufacturer in 1927 is preserved at the Cefn Coed Colliery Museum near Neath.

(Opposite): Section of the 1924 winding-house at Point of Ayr Colliery showing the typical elements of such a housing. The two sides of the engine sat on high piers extending through the engine-house basement which also housed the steam inlet and exhaust pipes. Overhead, in the main housing, was the hoist beam running on its elevated tracks to facilitate the raising of any parts of the engine requiring maintenance.

Water Pumping

The need for effective dewatering was a major inhibiting factor to the development of early mines. Slightly sloping tunnels or adits were cut below the working levels to drain water away to the surface, often emerging on the sides of valleys a considerable distance from the main workings. This was a common method employed in south Wales collieries until the mid-nineteenth century, but particularly at the deeper mines, and those around the coastal areas of Llanelli and the Swansea Valley, water had to be raised up the shafts. Each shaft was dug below the coal seam a short depth to give a sump in which water could collect, and at first it was simply wound out in barrels or buckets and emptied at the surface. Later, automatic valves were devised allowing speedier filling and emptying. From the sixteenth century, endless chains with buckets were introduced, or *'chain and rag'*, consisting of leather balls attached to an endless chain acting as a series of pistons to draw up water in a long pipe. Such machines were operated by waterwheel or horse-gin (i.e. engine), both common in Wales, or by gangs of men and occasionally by windmills. In Flintshire, for example, Edward Mostyn was using a water-powered 'chain and rag' pump from 1654 and Celia Fiennes noted the use of horse-gin-powered pumps at Holywell in 1698. In the eighteenth-century Llanelli coalfield it was recorded that horse-gins or waterwheels were used in a series to lift unwanted water upwards from mining tunnel to mining tunnel.[1]

Waterwheels on the surface were often used for both winding and pumping. A waterwheel at the Landore Pit, Swansea, provided power for both pumping and winding from the sinking of the colliery in 1754 until the installation of a Newcomen pumping engine in 1776, itself superseded by a huge Boulton and Watt pump in 1800. As was fairly common the waterwheel was retained for winding, until it was replaced by a small high-pressure Trevithick winder in 1803.[2] Water power in Wales

Many early nineteenth-century pumping-engines also served as colliery winders, such as this example surviving at the Glyn Pits near Pontypool, made in 1845 at the Neath Abbey Ironworks.

was a readily available resource and some collieries used waterwheels throughout the nineteenth-century as well.

That one of the earliest applications of steam power was for pumping illustrates the severe limitations put on the development of deep mines by the presence of unwanted water.

In 1698 Thomas Savery devised a practical steam-pump for drawing up water with a vacuum created by condensing steam in a cylinder, but it had a limited range of applications and there is no recorded use in a colliery in Wales. Of greater significance was Thomas Newcomen's atmospheric beam-engine, first installed at a mine in 1712 and widely employed, with improvements by James Watt, from 1765 until the late nineteenth century. The first in Wales was probably installed in 1717 by Lord Mansel at his Llansamlet (Swansea) collieries, the estimated annual upkeep of which was £120. Many more were introduced in the mid-eighteenth century. In the small Llanelli coalfield, for example, at least three atmospheric engines were erected between *ca*.1750 and *ca*.1769.[3] Whilst the larger coastal coalfield at Swansea had local engineers, such as Mr. Powell, manufacturing and adapting their own designs of atmospheric engine.

From 1775 the firm of Boulton & Watt made a considerable number of pumping-engines for mines and collieries. Many of these ponderous beam-engines were continuously at work in the coalfields, typically running at about eight strokes per minute, and operating a wooden pump-rod of bolted sections, to which was attached at the lower end a bucket or piston working at an 8ft. (2.44m.) stroke in a 2ft. (0.61m.) diameter pipe.[4] Larger than average was the Boulton and Watt engine installed at Landore, Swansea, in 1800 to replace a Newcomen engine of 1776 pumping through a 12in. (0.3m.) bore, which had eventually been overwhelmed by the pit flooding. The new 25h.p. engine had a 78in. (1.98m.) diameter cylinder and a 8-9 ft. (2.44-2.74m.) stroke, moving 1,100 gallons (5,000 litres) every minute with 12-13 strokes.[5] By about 1840 there were no less than three of these huge 65in. (1.65m.) plus cylinder engines in the Swansea Coalfield alone in addition to many lesser ones.[6] One of these was housed in the tall beam-engine house of Scott's Pit that still stands alongside the M4 motorway at Llansamlet, Swansea. The number of engine houses still standing in Wales conveys how common these beam-engines once were.

Water was raised in stages to the surface through pipes of wood, or later of cast iron, and discharged. The relative inefficiency of the engines and their high fuel consumption were tolerated; if the small coal or slack left after screening was not fed to the pumping-engine's boilers it would have been tipped away as there was no commercial demand for it.[7] In 1801 the plunger or ram was introduced which marked an important stage in pump development. The nature of pumping was changed from that of lifting to forcing, and the considerable weight of pump-rods was able to assist with the action instead of hindering it. Ram pumps were capable of exerting a much increased force than hitherto and could raise water to a greater height.

The prestige of new developments often obscured the fact that more conservative general practice lagged far behind. A survey of steam-engines carried out in the Neath and Swansea Valleys about 1840 enables us to obtain a fairly clear picture of contemporary practice.[8] Two of the Llansamlet Collieries (Swansea) still had 'common atmospheric engines'; one used for both pumping *and* winding. At that time one atmospheric engine had even been newly erected to power the pumps at the nearby 'Llanwern' Colliery; it was presumably the reuse of a much earlier engine. These by then 'antique' machines may well have dated back to the tenure of the Llansamlet Coalfield by London merchant Chauncey Townsend in the mid-eighteenth century, but the pithead availability of otherwise useless small coal made any still usable steam machine a useful capital asset. On the nearby Llanelli Coalfield, atmospheric engines were still being erected by the ironmaster, Alexander Raby, in the period from 1798 to 1808.[9]

By contrast only one of a total of seventeen recorded surface pumping-engines in the Swansea and Neath valleys of *ca.*1840 was a developed high-pressure engine, and only one other was recorded as a double-acting engine (with steam acting on the piston from both sides).

Interestingly enough no less than ten of the seventeen engines (59 per cent.) recorded in *ca.*1840 were combined pumping- *and* winding-engines. These were the type of combined engine manufactured in the mid- nineteenth century on the south Wales coalfield by the Neath Abbey Ironworks; an example can still be seen at the Glyn Pits, Pontypool.

In this *ca.*1840 survey one small (12in. (0.3m.) cylinder) high-pressure pump was also recorded underground at the Neath Abbey Colliery.

The Cornish boiler was developed from Trevithick's earlier work in 1813. It enabled higher steam pressures to be generated and allowed the expansive properties of steam to be exploited; compounding of engines subsequently became common. More sophisticated high-pressure Cornish beam-engines became common in the Welsh coalfields by the end of the nineteenth century, some as large as the 100in. (2.54m.) cylinder engine at Deep Navigation Colliery (1872-79).

Non-rotative pumping-engines, where the piston rod was connected directly to the pump rod, were prone to suffer serious damage if the load was suddenly lost by the pump drawing in air or by the breaking of a rod. The introduction in 1874 of Henry Davey's differential valve gear was an important development in the control of these engines, and led to production of the Hathorn Davey compound which could be supplied as single or triple expansion, with piston or ram-pump as required.[10] From the late nineteenth century similar horizontal engines became common, working counterbalanced pump rods through various bellcrank arrangements.

Rotative engines, where the reciprocating action of the steam piston was converted to rotary motion and back to reciprocating to drive the pump rods, could be run more efficiently and much faster than the non-rotative type as there was no danger of the piston overrunning. The Riedler pump of 1884, with its improved valve system, took advantage of the higher speeds available and made it possible to pump to over 2000ft. (610 m.) with an engine turning at 150 r.p.m.[11]

The trend was towards construction of self-contained pumps installed in a building at the bottom

Tall beam-engine pumping houses were often the most prominent features on nineteenth-century colliery sites (indeed more early examples survive in Wales than in the characteristic 'engine-house landscapes' of Cornwall). On many sites, as here at the British Ironworks, Abersychan, built by the Ebbw Vale Iron Company in 1845, they are all that remains of the collieries they once served. The engine illustrated below was a large low-pressure Boulton & Watt 78 in. (1.98 m.) diameter cylinder pumping engine built for the Swansea copper-smelting firm of Lockwood, Morris & Co. for their Landore coalpit in 1802. A wonder of its day, it was considered as a potential dual-purpose engine as were many in the early nineteenth century.
(Drawing by Hadyn Holloway based on the Boulton & Watt Collection, Birmingham Reference Library)

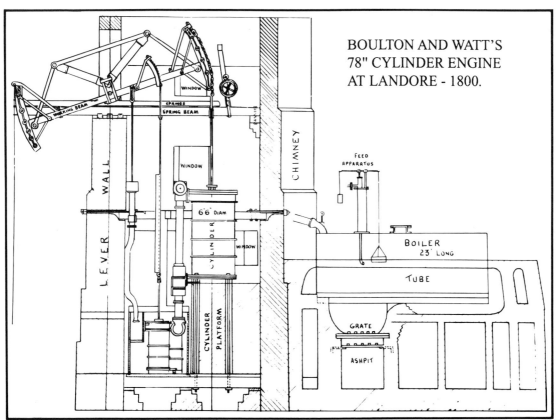

BOULTON AND WATT'S
78" CYLINDER ENGINE
AT LANDORE - 1800.

of the shaft, where the engine and pump were in one unit and close to their work. The problems associated with piping steam and exhaust in shafts encouraged development of other forms of power, and compressed air was successfully applied to drive pumps, particularly as auxiliaries. A further advantage of abandoning steam power was that the removal of cumbersome rods or steam pipes released the shaft for more productive uses.

For shaft-sinking, however, a portable pump was needed which could be lowered into the water as work progressed. The compact and lightweight Pulsometer used a combination of atmospheric pressure to draw water into alternate chambers and steam pressure to displace it through a delivery pipe; there were few moving parts and it could cope with sludge and dirty water typically encountered during sinking operations. In 1851 the centrifugal pump was introduced, requiring no conversion of motion and with no gearing or reciprocating valves, which could be driven at several hundred revolutions per minute by any form of power.[12]

Electricity was introduced for pumping on the south Wales border (at the Forest of Dean) in 1882, and a few years later the compact electric three-throw ram-pump appeared, often arranged for sinking suspended by chains, but also used as main pumps at many collieries. Because of the early application of electricity to drive small pumps, installed at several sites within a mine and linked to a pumping station near the pit bottom, there are relatively few extant pumping-engine houses at the surface. The most common pump now in use is the multi-stage centrifugal or turbine type, driven by electricity or compressed air as appropriate to its location, thoroughly reliable and capable of pumping away prodigious quantities of water. Although collieries may close for production of coal, pumping may have to be continued if there is a risk of flooding a neighbouring pit, and for this use submersible pumps are employed at the closed shaft.

References :

1   M.V. Symons, *Coal-Mining in the Llanelli Area, Vol.I. 16th Century to 1829* (Llanelli, 1979), p.314.

2   John Morris's Commonplace Book, 26 January 1775, Morris Manuscripts, University College Swansea, Library; L.B. Collier, 'A Detailed Survey of the History and Development of the South Wales Coal Industry (from 1750-1850) (University of London Ph.D. thesis, 1940), p.28.

3   A.H. John, *The Industrial Development of South Wales 1750-1850* (Cardiff, 1950), p.6, and M.V Symons, *Coal Mining in Llanelli,* p.317.

4   D. Anderson, *Coal* (Newton Abbot, 1971), p.44.

5   John Morris's Commonplace Book, 29 July 1776, Morris Manuscripts, University College Swansea Library; W.G. Thomas, MS History of South Wales Coalmines, p.95, Welsh Industrial and Maritime Museum; R.P. Roberts, 'History of Coalmining in Gower from 1700 to 1832' (University of Wales (Cardiff), M.A.thesis, 1953), p.110 quoting statistics of John Buddle, mining engineer; E.T. Svedenstierna, *Svedenstierna's Tour of Great Britain 1802-3,* p.46.

6   'Statistical Table of Steam Power, Swansea' (Swansea Museum (RISW), Morgan MSS).

7   D. Anderson, *Coal,* p.43.

8   'Statistical Table of Steam Power, Swansea'.

9   Symons, *Coal-Mining in the Llanelli Area,* p.317.

10   W.S.Boulton (ed), *Practical Coal Mining* (London 1907-09), vol. iii, p.180.

11   W.S.Boulton (ed), *Practical Coal Mining,* vol. iv, p.220.

12   ibid.

(Opposite): Hathorn-Davey horizontal pumping-engines were replacing cumbersome beam-engine pumps by the end of the nineteenth century and were often inconspicuously placed in the basements of steam-winding houses. Examples still remain at the Marine and Llanover Hall Colliery sites in Gwent.

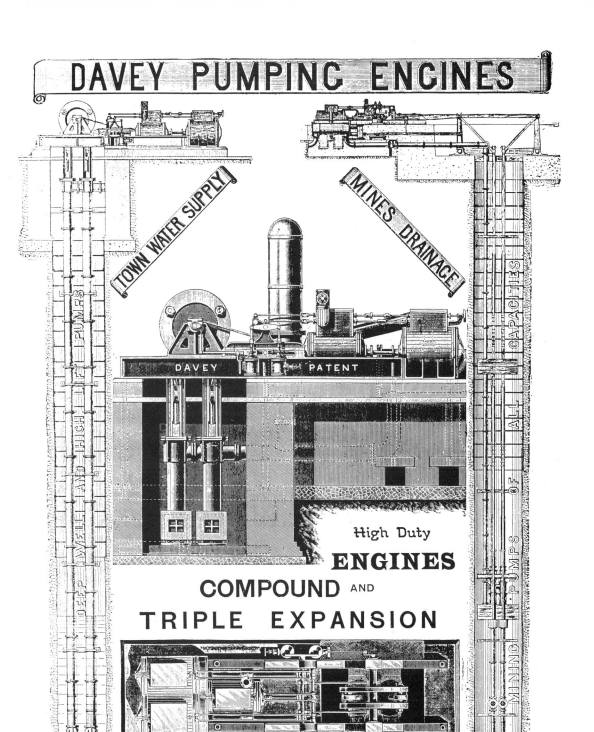

DAVEY PUMPING ENGINES

TOWN WATER SUPPLY

MINES DRAINAGE

DEEP WELL AND HIGH LIFT PUMPS

MINING PUMPS OF ALL CAPACITIES

DAVEY PATENT

High Duty
ENGINES
COMPOUND AND
TRIPLE EXPANSION

HYDRAULIC MACHINERY

HATHORN, DAVEY & CO.,
3, PRINCE'S STREET, WESTMINSTER, LONDON, S.W.,
And **LEEDS.**

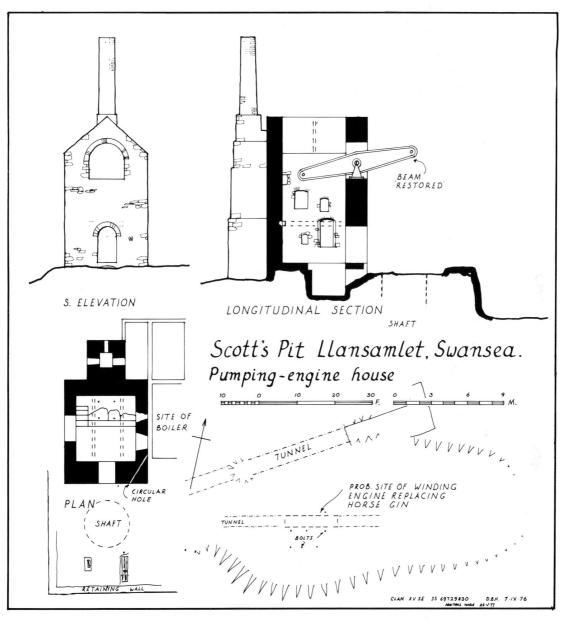

S. ELEVATION

LONGITUDINAL SECTION

BEAM RESTORED

SHAFT

Scott's Pit Llansamlet, Swansea.
Pumping-engine house

SITE OF BOILER

PLAN

SHAFT

CIRCULAR HOLE

RETAINING WALL

TUNNEL

TUNNEL

BOLTS

PROB. SITE OF WINDING ENGINE REPLACING HORSE GIN

GLAM XV SE 55 69729830   D.B.H. 7·IX·76
ADDITIONS MADE 26·V·77

Scott's Pit, Llansamlet, Swansea, is now a prominent landmark alongside the M4 motorway but the tall beam-engine house was built in 1817-19 to house a low-pressure Boulton and Watt steam-engine pump. It had a high-pressure engine fitted in 1872 and continued intermittently in use with various engines until 1930. The photograph opposite shows the site under excavation and consolidation in 1976-80; an exercise which revealed an early haystack-boiler base to the left of the engine house. The plan above shows the site of a later Cornish boiler of ca.1872 and also the small tunnel that led to a later winder replacing the original horse-powered winding-gin. A second tunnel from the shaft terminated in a ventilation chimney.

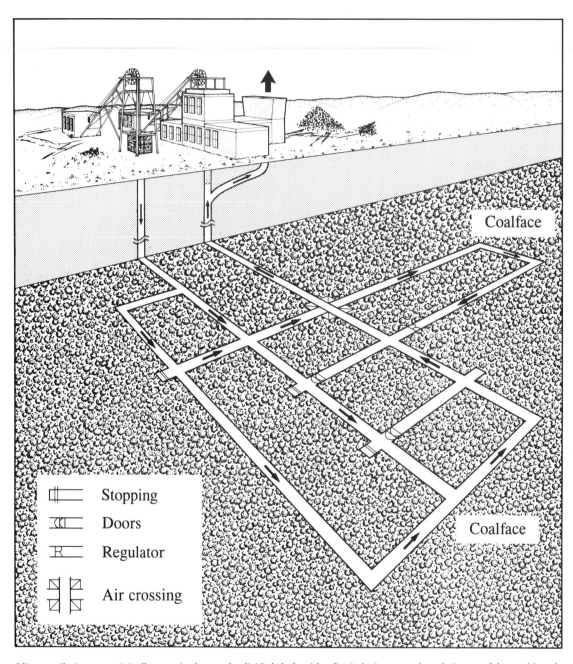

Stopping

Doors

Regulator

Air crossing

Coalface

Coalface

Mine ventilation was originally conceived around a divided shaft, with a fire inducing an updraught in one of the partitioned sections of the shaft. The diagram above shows a later stage of the development of the system with separate downcast and upcast shafts, the latter capped by an airtight casing. Air was drawn through a side tunnel (the 'fan drift') linked to the upcast shaft. Airtight doors and crossings ensured that the induced airflow prevented the build-up of dangerous gases or stale air in any of the active headings and coalfaces in a mine.

Mine Ventilation

Mine ventilation is a highly specialized subject to which many text books have been devoted. The physical features associated with directing and controlling air movement underground are not of great engineering or architectural significance, unlike the technology and comparatively sophisticated machinery employed to generate the flow of air.

There are several reasons for ventilating mines: to bring oxygen to the men, to remove dangerous gas, to extract dust and fumes caused by mining operations, and for cooling - for each 40m. in depth, the temperature rises 1° C, the average depth of a UK mine being 450m. Development of coal mines was hampered by, amongst other factors, the shortcomings of the technology available to improve the ventilation at depths where the rich coal seams lay. Pits in south Wales were notably gaseous, and effective ventilation was a constant challenge, increasingly so from the mid-nineteenth century as mines became deeper. Some of the worst mining disasters caused by the explosion of gas or coal dust occurred in south Wales at this time. Such explosions killed twelve miners at Dinas Colliery in 1844; 28 at Thomas Powell's Duffryn Colliery in 1845; 35 at Risca in 1846; 20 at Eaglebush in 1848; and 52 at Llety Shenkin in 1849.[1]

Output of ventilating devices is usually measured in cubic feet per minute (c.f.m.) or cubic metres per second (m^3/sec), and in a modern colliery an average throughput of 7000m^3 of air were needed for each ton of coal mined, illustrating the importance of effective ventilation in the coal industry.

The earliest form of ventilation was entirely natural and relied upon temperature differences in the shafts causing circulation of air through the mine, the flow changing direction from winter to summer. To allow control over such seasonal vagaries and to increase the quantity of air passing through the mines, furnace ventilation was devised whereby a fire was made at the bottom of one shaft, the rising hot gases and smoke drawing fresh air via a second shaft through the mine. A safer development of this technique, although not universal, was to set the furnace under a chimney stack on the surface and link it to the upcast shaft by a short tunnel. Surviving chimneys of this latter type include examples in the Rhondda, at the Marine Colliery site (Cwm) and at Cwm Pelenna. The use of such primitive methods was common until the end of the nineteenth century. In 1875 Thomas Forster Brown told the South Wales Institute of Engineers that the normal method of ventilation was still by furnace. However, by 1892 he could assert that *'mechanical ventilation by exhausting the air by fans erected on the surface is rapidly replacing the furnace placed at the shaft bottom.'* The large south Wales coalfield was by then a model for other British coalfields in this respect.[2]

Early mechanical means of ventilation employed bellows of leather or tarred cloth on a timber frame as a form of pump to force fresh air down wooden pipes and into the workings, and were at first human- or animal-powered (although Agricola had noted small bellows ventilators driven by water wheels in use in German mines in the sixteenth century). In 1743 horse-driven bellows producing a respectable 3000c.f.m. (1.4m^3/sec) were working at a County Durham mine.[3] The late eighteenth century saw the development of new ways of directing air through the workings, through use of one-way doors, air crossings (where an intake airway crossed a return without leakage between the two), better stoppings to seal off old workings, brattice cloths to direct air into side roadways and regulators to control the flow. Furnace ventilation was widely applied, and by 1850 was in common use despite the limited capacity, corrosive effect on ropes and fittings in shafts, obvious danger and great fuel consumption. From the mid-nineteenth century, mechanical ventilators gradually replaced furnaces, although coal-owners in south Wales were particularly resistant to change. A survey made in the area at the end of the century showed that the use of furnace and natural ventilation considerably outnumbered mechanical means. The last British ventilation furnace, in Staffordshire, did not go out of use until 1950.[4]

Availability of steam power enabled great increases in capacity to be realized - the first steam-driven

rotating ventilators, at Walker Colliery on Tyneside, appeared in 1769 [5] - although the methods of application of this power to ventilation were diverse. The period between 1835 and 1852 saw much experiment in south Wales with mechanical ventilation; in 1848 William Struvé, a mining engineer of Swansea, developed an 1810 design by John Taylor into an economical air pump for ventilating mines.[6] Several were constructed, the first of 13,500c.f.m. (6.3m^3/sec.) capacity in 1849 at Eaglebush Colliery near Neath,[7] and the largest at Wynnstay Colliery where two 24ft. (7.31m.) cylinders moved 70,000c.f.m. (32.7m^3/sec.), replacing a furnace.

The first steam-driven fan is thought to date from 1837 when a design by William Fourness was installed near Leeds.[8] In 1849 William Brunton erected a Fourness fan, with its axle vertical, over Gelligaer Colliery shaft, and shortly after James Nasmyth erected a similar fan at Abercarn Colliery, but running in the now familiar fashion with a horizontal axle.[9]

In 1859 John Nixon designed and installed at his Deep Duffryn Colliery a reciprocating ventilator, comprising twin wooden pistons running horizontally on wheels inside two large rectangular chambers. However, the rotative fan was clearly becoming the most effective, economical and reliable method of providing ventilation, and 1864 saw the British introduction of a type which was to become virtually the industry standard. M. Guibal, a Belgian mining engineer, had developed by 1859 the most reliable ventilating fan of the period. One of its more important features was the expanding chimney or évasée to lower the final velocity of exhaust air. The Schiele fan, with its spiral exhaust chamber, appeared shortly afterwards and with the Guibal and open-running Waddle fan were the three most common types in use in Britain at the end of the nineteenth century. Walker Brothers of Wigan were licensed to build Guibal fans, and improved the design over a period so that in 1887 they were able to patent their 'Indestructible' fan, combining the best features from the Guibal and Schiele; many other designs appeared, all basically similar but with

(Opposite): The distinctive layout of a colliery fan installation with enclosed airtight fan drifts (tunnels) leading from the shaft in the foreground to the circular fan casings and prominent évasée outlets above the engine house beyond (Lady Windsor Colliery).

detailed differences, each manufacturer claiming an advantage over the products of his rivals.

Introduction of the electric motor to mining towards the end of the nineteenth century allowed development of the axial-flow fan, first appearing at a colliery in Northumberland in 1896.[10]

Henceforth, no new methods of ventilation were devised, advances concentrating on improving the efficiency of existing types. As higher-speed steam- and electric engines became available, the tendency was for fans to be built smaller and rotate faster, but with increased output.

Because of the need to provide more powerful ventilation as collieries were linked underground during general modernization of the industry from the 1950s, systems were uprated by the replacement of steam-engines with electric motors or, particularly with new schemes and extensive remodellings, complete new fans and drives were installed. However, old systems were sometimes retained for back-up as at Six Bells Colliery, linked to Marine and Blaenserchan in the 1970s, where the fan used during the sinking of the shaft and its two later replacements were retained until closure.

More effective ventilation allowed extra coal faces to be worked on the same level, and mine productivity could be increased subject to transport and winding limitations. Moreover, applied in conjunction with developments in pumping technology, it enabled coal to be mined at greater depths and avoided the need to work poorer quality seams near the surface, thus preventing a probable decline in total output.

Technical Development

As each mine has different physical, geological and aerodynamic characteristics and a unique layout, so each has its individual ventilation requirements, although underlying principles are common to all. Fans in Britain are traditionally exhausting ventilators, and draw in fresh air via the downcast shaft, through the mine to the working faces by the intake airways, and out through the fan by return airways and the upcast shaft. Normally coal-winding is on the downcast shaft, and services, men and materials use the upcast. An airtight casing, at first simply a wooden lid lifted by the rising cage and later fixed fireproof steel cladding, is needed around the upcast shaft top to prevent air being drawn straight into the fan without first circulating through the mine, and an adjoining chamber fitted with a set of double doors is essential as an airlock.

Fans were set in a side passage, called the fan drift, to avoid risk of damage by any explosion travelling up the main shaft, and also to avoid interference with other activities at the shaft top. Provision had to be made for reversal of the air current in the mine for emergency fire control, and this was usually effected with various arrangements of doors and shutters in the fan drift. Independent fans or duplicate engines were necessary; as mines had to be kept ventilated continuously to prevent a build-up of gas, so reliable equipment was essential. At Penallta Colliery, for example, a through-flow of 720 million cubic feet (20.16 million m^3) of air per day was maintained.[11]

Two main types of fan were used latterly at Welsh collieries: centrifugal and axial-flow. There are numerous designs of centrifugal fan, either enclosed or open-running, although all draw in air through the centre, on either one side (single inlet) or both sides (double inlet), and expel it at the edge through an expanding-section outlet or évasée.

The most widely used and known open-running design was made by the Waddle Patent Fan and Engineering Co. of Llanelli, who also built steam-engines to drive their fans. Introduction of the Waddle was an original and important contribution by the engineering industry in Wales. It was cheap to build and install, and also remarkably efficient in action. Being a single-inlet type, the backward-curving blades expelled air through out-turned rims, having the same effect as an évasée. The Waddle was originally a large slow-running fan, but continuous improvements were made and the diameter much reduced for the same capacity. At Morfa Colliery, for example, a 21ft. (6.40m.) Waddle replaced an older 40ft. (12.19m.) version and not only increased the air flow through the mine but was more economical to run.[12] The first was installed in south Wales at Bonville's Court Colliery in 1863, and the last steam-driven Waddle to operate was at Deep Duffryn Colliery, Mountain Ash.

Of the enclosed types, all are developments of the basic Guibal fan which consisted of 8 or 10 wooden paddles bolted to cast-iron arms fitted into a wooden hub. Air was admitted on one side, the other being connected to the drive. The Guibal Fan house at Cwmbran Colliery, believed to date from about 1880, contained a 30ft. (9.14m.) diameter by 10ft. (3.05m.) wide fan driven, unusually, by a vertical steam-engine. A similar sized house of the same date stands in a ruinous condition at Ynyscedwyn Colliery, West Glamorgan.[13]

Walker Brothers steel 'Indestructible' fan was a double-inlet type with eight blades, set in a spiral casing with an évasée. Examples remain at the impressive Crumlin Navigation Colliery, Gwent, built in 1911 to house two fans 24ft. (7.32m.) in diameter by 8ft. (2.44m.) wide, each driven by a triple-compound steam-engine.[14]

In 1898 the much superior Sirocco fan was developed and installed widely as at, for example, Lewis Merthyr (1907) and Penallta (1910), both in use until recent closure, and a pair were installed underground at Taff Merthyr Colliery as recently as 1978. Tests carried out at Pelton Colliery, Durham, showed the considerable advantage of the Sirocco over traditional types: two Guibal fans, of 30 and 36ft. (9.14 and 10.97m.) diameter and turning at 62 and 52 r.p.m. respectively, required 12.5 h.p. (9325 watts) *more* input to move an average of 24,140 c.f.m. (675.9 m^3/sec.) *less* air than one 75in. (1.90m.) diameter double-inlet Sirocco fan running at 294 r.p.m.[15] Design development was thus towards smaller, faster fans with more capacity and requiring less power; amongst others, Capell, Keith, Rateau, and Turbon types are all known to have worked at collieries in Wales,[16] and represent a few of the many types available.

Axial-flow fans are set inside the airway and draw through rotary airscrews, originally simple aeroplane-type propellers which have developed into sophisticated multi-vaned turbines. Driving-belts from an external engine had to be shielded from the air flow, although suitably flame-proofed electric motors could be mounted in the airway and coupled directly to the impeller. Although rare as a main fan, extensive use of this type was made in south Wales as an underground booster from the 1970s.

As ventilating fans run best at a constant high speed and offer a steady load, power requirements are straightforward and ultimately ideally suited to electric drive. Previously, compound condensing steam-engines were coupled directly to large slow fans and later with leather-belt drives to smaller fans then coming into use; eventually cotton rope or vee belts on multi-groove pulleys were used to drive high-speed fans as electric power became widespread.

References:

1   J. Williams, 'The Coal Industry, 1750-1914', *Glamorgan County History, Vol. v, Industrial Glamorgan*, pp.155-210.
2   ibid.
3   The Colliery Guardian, 18 February 1927.
4   A.R. Griffin, *Coalmining* (London, 1971), p.71.
5   R.L. Galloway, *A History of Coal Mining in Great Britain* (London, 1882), p.107.
6   The Colliery Guardian, 12 June 1858, p.374.
7   B. Job, 'Colliery Ventilation by Steam Power', *International Stationary Steam Engine Bulletin xiv*, p.25.
8   ibid., p.24.
9   Galloway, *History of Coal Mining,* p.254.
10 Job, *'Colliery Ventilation'*, p.38.
11 G.C. Hann, 'The Sinking and Equipping of Penallta Colliery', *Proceedings of the South Wales Institute of Engineers* XXVII (1910), p.53.
12 C.M.Percy, *The Mechanical Equipment of Colleries* (Manchester, 1905), pp. 278-9. Original drawings of Waddle Fans are in the Waddle Engineering Company MSS in Swansea University College Library.
13 N.A. Chapman, 'Ventilation of Mines', *Industrial Archaeology Review* XV (1992), p.47.
14 ibid., p52.
15 A.L. Stevens, 'The Sirocco Fan', *Proceedings of the South Wales Institute of Engineers* XXIV (1907), p.111.
16 D.& J.S. Penman, *Mine Ventilation* (London, 1947), p.167 et seq.

The colliery ventilation chimney was a common feature on eighteenth- and early nineteenth-century collieries.
This nineteenth-century example of a ventilation furnace and chimney survives at Trehafod in the Rhondda.
(John Cornwell)

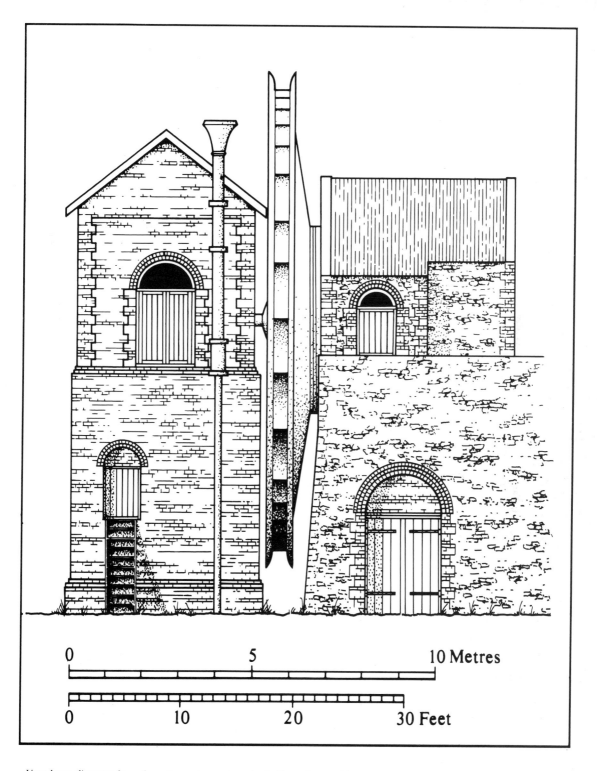

Very large diameter fans of varying makes were typical of late nineteenth-century ventilation practice. This was the 42ft. (12.8 m.) diameter Waddle Fan at Deep Duffryn Colliery. The air was drawn through the encased fan drift on the right and the fan was powered from the engine house on the left.

THE WADDLE
IMPROVED PATENT
FANS

With SIMPLE and COMPOUND ENGINES, to Circulate up to 800,000 Cubic Feet of Air per Minute.

ADVANTAGES.

Capacity for Maintaining High Water Gauges at Low Periphery Speed. Very high useful effect.
Entire Freedom from Vibration, which is the case with no other Fan. Absolutely Noiseless.
No troublesome Belt or other Gearing.
Small quantity of Masonry required.
Repairs never necessary.
Non-liability to Accident from any cause.

PATENTEES AND SOLE MAKERS—
WADDLE PATENT FAN & ENGINEERING CO.,
LLANMORE WORKS, LLANELLY.

(Above): Photograph of the 'spare' fan engine at Deep Duffryn Colliery: in the background the crankshaft of the Waddle Fan is connected to the twin engine at the far end. The connecting rod would be transferred from the crosshead of one engine to the other whenever maintenance or servicing was required on one of the engines. The advertisement on the left publicised these Llanelli-made engines in 'The Colliery Guardian' for 1900.

(Opposite): The enclosed Guibal fan house was distinguished by its distinctive receding arches which were the masonry support for the expanding upward snout of the évasée chimney, as here at Upper Cwmbran Colliery. (drawing from C.M.Percy, 'The Mechanical Equipment of Colleries', p.282)

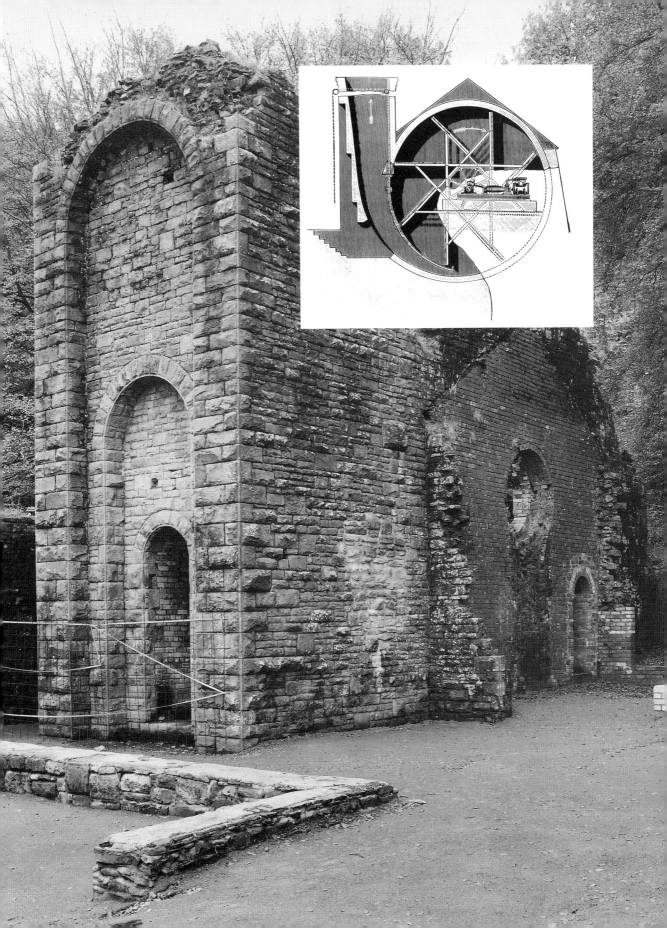

(Opposite page): Early small-size propellor fan at Six Bells Colliery (1891).

(Below): The design drawings for Britannia Colliery (1910-14) show that the drive from the original electric motor was to consist of seven $1^1/_2$ in. (38mm) diameter ropes. Interestingly what survived in 1989 (see photo) was a leather-belt transmission complete with tensioning mechanism. Generally it has been considered that leather-belt transmission was superseded firstly by multiple cotton-rope drive and then by multiple vee-belts.
(British Coal drawings, Glamorgan Archives Service)

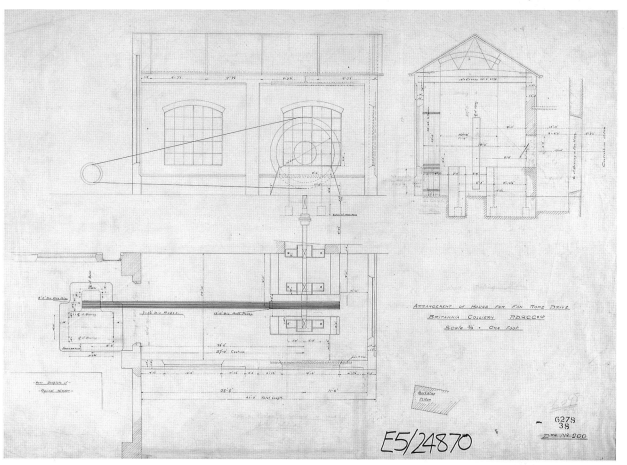

E5/24870

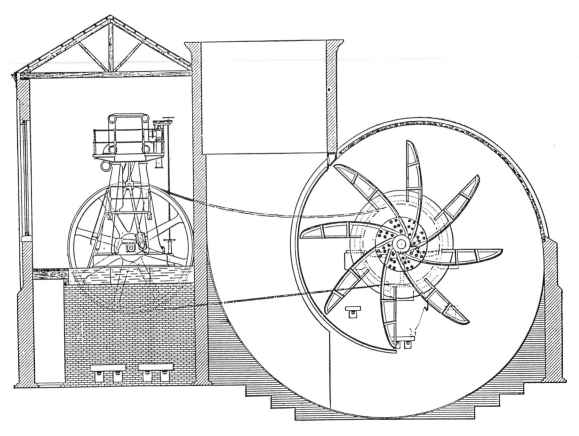

(Above): The fan house at Crumlin Navigation Colliery was, and is, part of the finest group of colliery buildings in Wales.
The fan house in the foreground is distinguished by the square vent of the Walker fan which is still in situ although the large
four-cylinder triple expansion fan engine of 1908 is now in the Welsh Industrial and Maritime Museum at Cardiff.
Illustrated above left is a drawing of a Walker fan and its drive. ('Practical Coal Mining' , p.556)
(Opposite below): Multiple cotton-rope drive to the axle of a fan as used on the older electrically driven fan engine
at Six Bells Colliery.

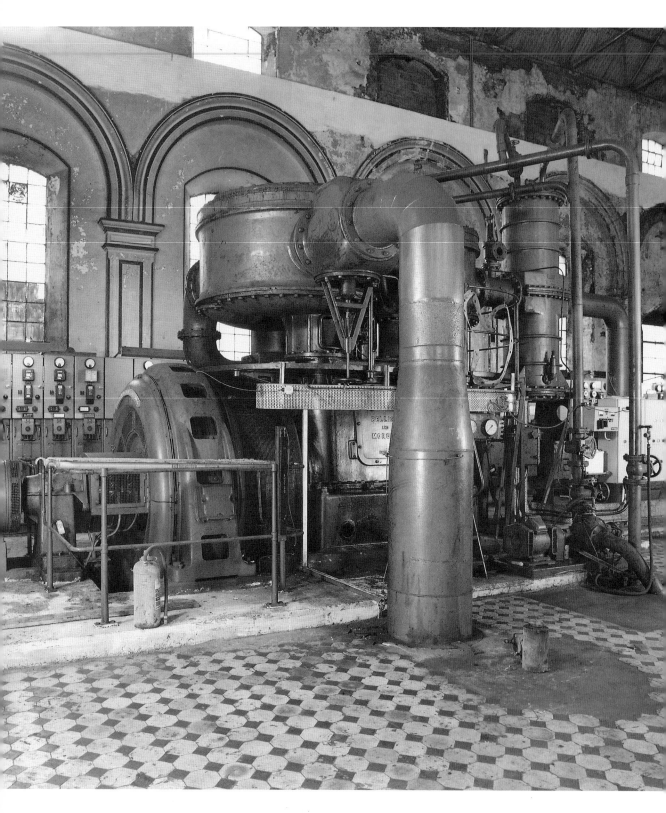

The Use of Compressed Air

Steam seemed the obvious power source to drive machinery underground, as it had been applied successfully to surface-based pumping and winding installations since 1712. However, the drawbacks to operating steam-powered equipment in a mine were considerable. The most obvious disadvantage of placing the boilers underground near the engine was the risk of fire and explosion. Although expelling waste steam and smoke up a shaft along with heat from the boilers might improve the air flow, in practice exhaust gases were found to have a corrosive effect on shaft linings and cables. Alternatively, if the boilers were at surface level, steam had to be piped down the shafts involving great heat loss, and hence power reduction, not least through leaky pipe joints. However, steam power was applied on a limited scale underground: Hendreforgan and Llansamlet collieries in the Swansea Valley were two of the first to mechanize their haulage in the main headings,[1] and a large mid-nineteenth-century stone-vaulted enginehouse can still be seen at Big Pit, Blaenavon. Application of steam was unsuited to portable machinery because of the large diameter steam-tight pipes required and the heat given off by such equipment. These disadvantages led to the development of the steam-engine-driven compressor, and use of the more manageable energy of compressed air in the mines. Its first major use was for providing haulage of the coal trams in the main heading tunnels.

Compressed air was first employed successfully in a French coal mine in 1845, when it was transmitted a distance of 750ft. (228.45m.). Its use soon became widespread and in 1849 the pneumatic rock-drill was invented in the USA. Compressed air was first applied at the large Dowlais Ironworks collieries in 1857 and by 1874 there were 26 compressed-air haulage engines in collieries owned by Powell Duffryn alone.[2] Pneumatic tools and machinery of all sorts were developed - hand-picks,(introduced to south Wales in the mid 1920s), longwall coal cutters,

heading boring-machines, door and gate controllers, tram tipplers, braking systems for winders - and compressed air is still a valuable power source in modern collieries, despite extensive electrification. Its over-riding advantage against the alternatives of steam or electricity is almost complete safety.

Compressors are either of the rotary-turbo or reciprocating-piston type, compound versions of the latter being by far the most common. Cooling of the output air, usually by passing it through a water-jacket, is necessary as an enormous amount of heat is generated during compression. Temperature reduction of the air between the low- and high-pressure cylinders is effected by an intercooler, and of final output from the high-pressure cylinder by an aftercooler. High temperatures tended to increase the volume and hence reduce the effectiveness of the pressurised air. Conversely, at the 'working' end, air exhausted from a pneumatic tool or machine cooled rapidly on release and caused problems with ice formation. To obviate this compressed air is stored in an air receiver, consisting of a large steel tank or reservoir, which allows moisture to be drained off at intervals and which fulfills several other purposes. Air can be stored in the receiver to meet peak demands, and storage acts as a buffer eliminating the potentially damaging effect of surges from the compressors upon transmission pipes and joints.

A typical installation of the late nineteenth century consisted of a horizontal compound steam-engine driving a two-stage reciprocating compressor, although many variations were to be found: in-line or side-by-side arrangement of engine and compressor, single or double acting, single or multi-stage, with inter-coolers and after-coolers. The most successful type in the twentieth century, very popular in south Wales and still at work in many collieries until recent closures, was the Bellis & Morcom vertical two-stage reciprocating compressor, electrically driven, with either intermediate or after-cooler.

Compressed air was vital to so many aspects of working a mine that several compressors were usually installed; sufficient stand-by capacity had to be available

(Opposite): Electrically-driven Belliss and Morcom
two-stage compressor with after-cooler at Penallta Colliery.

at all times. Compressors and their power supply were often housed in a large dedicated building before the advent of common power-halls where they were normally set in the centre of the building between the winding-engines.

References
1   J. Williams, 'The Coal Industry, 1750-1914', *The Glamorgan County History, Vol.5, Industrial Glamorgan*, pp.155-210.
2   The Colliery Guardian, 1926, p.959.

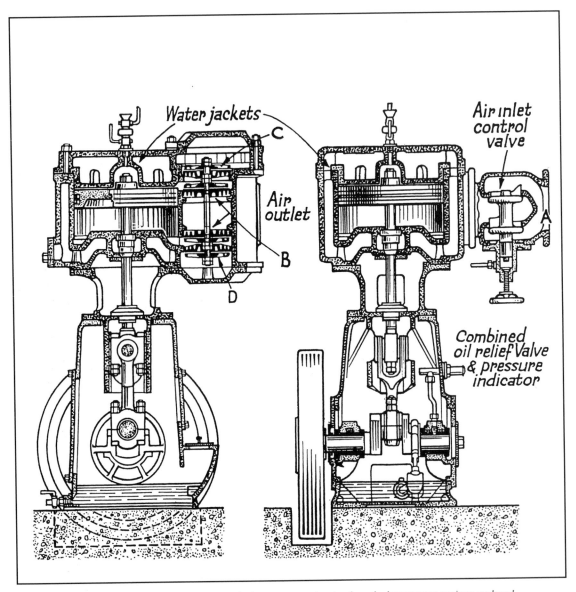

The internal workings of a Bellis and Morcom vertical compressor showing how the large upper-casings enclosed air-compressing pistons encased in a cooling jacket of water. The inlet and exhaust valves consist of thin spring-steel discs covering multiple ports in cast-iron valve seats; 'B' represents the two exhaust valves, 'C' & 'D' are the inlet valves, and the automatic suction valve 'A' opens under its own weight.
(T.R.Barnard, 'Mechanical Engineering', 'Coal Mining', (London,1954), p.231)

Tandem unit of two Belliss and Morcom two-stage compressors with inter-coolers, at Six Bells Colliery (1891), driven by a large electric motor. There were five compressors (a single and two tandem units) at the colliery indicating the importance given to the continuous supply of compressed air. These were housed in a large detached building.

Preparation of Coal for Sale

In a typical mid-Victorian colliery the preparation of coal for the market would consist of the manual removal of larger stones and other unwanted debris, followed by screening into various sizes and tipping into railway trucks for transport off site. The process was extremely wasteful as small coal and dust would be deliberately left in the mine or, if brought to the surface, tipped on a convenient piece of land nearby with only a small amount supplying the boilers of the collieries. This practice continued in some places until the 1930s.[1]

However, riddles, coarse sieves or small screens on the surface were also used from an early period. In Pembrokeshire at the beginning of the seventeenth century, a small pit employing 16 people would employ two riddlers who riddled the coal when it was wound up, first drawing the small coal from the big by one kind of riddle, the second riddling with a smaller riddle drawing small coals for the smiths from the culm.[2] Larger fixed screens at surface level did not appear until late in the nineteenth century. Early colliery owners wanted only clean (i.e. free from dust), large lumps; small coal and slack were unsaleable. Coal was raised to the surface and tipped or shovelled directly into carts, wagons or boats for transport to the market. As the nineteenth century progressed, a slow mechanization and refinement of coal-handling took place. A demand grew for different grades, and the simplest way of achieving this was by tipping the coal over inclined metal bars, spaced according to the size of product required, sometimes with a 'picking belt' where larger pieces or stones could be removed by hand from a moving conveyor. Gradually, the more effective vibrating screens were introduced, and installation of manual, then powered, rotary tipplers

(Opposite): A typical coal-preparation complex could have miles of conveyor belts with covered housings. Pictured is a 'transfer house' used for changing the direction of conveyors or for adding material to an existing flow. A belt entered at high level (right) and tipped to another below; sometimes, as here, the opportunity was taken to provide an overflow to the ground in order to regulate the flow of material (Oakdale Colliery).

to empty the trams of coal eliminated the back-breaking labour of shovelling coal onto the screens. Railway track layouts evolved into multi-level gravity-assisted or powered systems whereby trams of coal were pushed, one after the other, through the tipplers and continued around a circuit, controlled by retarders and hauled automatically by engine-driven inclines or 'creepers' to a higher level for eventual return to the shaft top.[3]

Particularly with the advent of skip-winding in the late 1930s,[4] and wider use of coal-preparation plants to supplement the screens, it was found most expedient to transport coal from the pithead for further processing by means of conveyor belts, introduced in about 1900 but not widely applied.[5] The operation of a modern preparation and washing plant is continuous and requires the coal to arrive at a reasonably constant rate, best achieved by a system of conveyors and transfer houses.

The uneven application of this technology resulted in differing levels of mechanization of coal handling between collieries; factors causing this were the natural reluctance to change an existing system with the accompanying disruption to production, high capital costs of new equipment, the ready availability of cheap man- and woman-power, and the requirements of the customer. Despite the attractions of cheaper production, better quality output or increased capacity, it is often surprising how long the old methods persisted after a new process or item of equipment became available, except when legislation and latterly market demands forced changes.

The concept of washing was introduced in about 1870 to clean the coal for coke-making, but increasing mechanization, market demands and simple economics forced the technology to develop and enable ever more of the coal to be recovered until nowadays even the finest particles of dust are extracted for use, and only stones and shale are discarded. Mechanized coal-cutting is not as discriminating as the miner with his hand-pick and removes the whole seam, including the shale which may account for up to 40 per cent. of the material wound to the surface for processing.[6] Because much of the most profitable high-quality coal has been worked out, more inferior coals are now being cut which require proper washing and careful blending to produce a saleable product for the market. With the gradual decline of steam power in industry, particularly in the 1950s, the electricity-generating power-stations emerged as the main customers for coal and became increasingly discriminating in the quality and consistency of coal they needed, specifying carefully and monitoring what they were receiving. During the same period, after nation-alization, it was realised that collieries no longer needed to offer several grades of coal for sale but could specialize in supplying specific markets. Efficient high-capacity washeries were built and individual mines could concentrate on production of only a narrow range of coal, or even just a single grade, with attendant savings in capital outlay and operating costs. Also, new coal grades were being developed. For example, provision of suitable quality coals for manufactured smokeless fuel was forced upon the industry after the introduction of the 1956 Clean Air Act which led to demand for the high output of a carefully controlled product, best achieved from a few

Trams of coal direct from the pit (Six Bells Colliery) were clamped in the tippler and bodily inverted over a conveyor (to the left) which formerly transferred the coal direct to the screens, latterly to a washery.

dedicated collieries rather than having production spread widely throughout the industry.

The number of coal-cleaning installations in Britain increased sharply between 1920 and 1938. Plant varied between coalfields, local collieries responding to the results obtained by trials of one type introduced to their area, sometimes merely by the persuasiveness of sales representatives. Although several types of varying sophistication and complexity are still in use today, the underlying principles of separating coal from shale are reasonably straightforward, and in general are based on the fact that shale is heavier than coal. Gravity separation is usually a wet process using, for example, such highly specialized equipment as jigs, launders, upward-current classifiers or dense-medium separators, but can be carried out dry with air jigs or pneumatic tables. Other methods using magnetic attraction or electrical conductivity, or the froth flotation process relying on surface properties, are also used.[7]

Some early washing methods used shaking troughs to separate the coal and shale with a degree of success, but used a considerable amount of water. However, jigs are the oldest form of concentrating device and the most widespread; the principle uses an up and down current of water passing through the material to be separated. The Sheppard Washer, made in south Wales and common there at the end of the nineteenth century, was an example of a partial application of the process.[8] Greater success of the Baum jig, developed from 1880, was through the use of compressed air to create the pulses in the water tank in such a manner as to prevent the coal and shale particles recombining after each stroke, as happened in the previous direct plunger systems. In one operation a Baum jig could treat coal sizes from dust to 4in. (100mm.). Complete Baum washing plants were erected at numerous collieries as a steel-framed building on columns above the railway tracks; coal was brought to the top after preliminary treatment and washed, screened, drained, stored and loaded without further lifting by elevator or conveyor, so reducing handling to a minimum. Slurry was allowed to settle in distinctive large conical tanks where clean water overflowed and was reused in the washing process, while concentrated slurry was removed for tipping or further processing.

Another wet process, the Chance method introduced from the U.S.A., was used mainly on anthracite and bituminous coals and was common in south Wales. Sand is used as the dense medium, suspended artificially in a conical tank of water and creating a specific gravity between that of coal and shale; when dirty coal is added, the clean coal rises and shale particles sink, allowing both to be removed.

The important technique of froth flotation was recognized in 1860 and introduced from about 1906.[9] It depends upon differences in surface characteristics of coal and shale and is used in conjunction with other washing processes for separating very fine particles. Dirty coal dust and a small amount of oil are mixed in a tank of water and small air bubbles are introduced which attach themselves only to the coal particles, carrying them to the surface while the shale sinks to the bottom. The coal froth is skimmed off and recovered in the form of a dried cake (known as 'fines') by means of rotary vacuum drums, then blended with larger sizes or used as pulverized fuel.[10]

References:

1 A.R. Griffin, *The British Coalmining Industry*, (London, 1971), p.105.

1 W.Rees, Industry before the Industrial Revolution, (Cardiff, 1968), vol.1 p.123

3 C.M. Percy, *The Mechanical Equipment of Collieries*, (Manchester, 1905), p.608 et seq.

4 'The Centenary of Qualter Hall', *The Colliery Guardian*, (1960), p.539.

5 D. Anderson, *Coal: A Pictorial History of the British Coal Industry*, (Newton Abbot, 1982), p.35.

6 A. Grounds, 'Progress in Coal Preparation Practice', *The Colliery Guardian*, (March 1947), pp. 251-255 and 289-291.

7 H.H. Lowry (ed.), *Chemistry of Coal Utilisation* (National Research Council Committee, 1945), chap. 16.

8 C.M. Percy, *op cit.* p.661.

9 S.H. North, *Modern Coal Cleaning Plant*, (1932).

10 J. Sinclair, *Planning and Mechanised Drifting at Collieries*, (1977), pp.218-220.

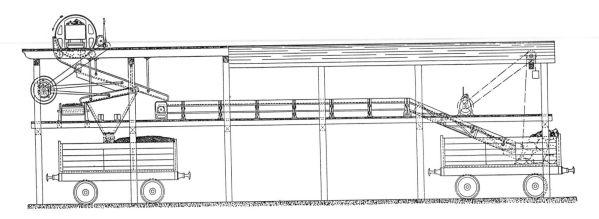

One of the problems of late nineteenth-and early twentieth-century coal handling was how to get the coal from the tram-circuit at the shaft-head, sort it by size and pick out shale, and then load it into standard-gauge railway wagons for transit off site. The drawing above shows a tram from the pit being rotated on an upper level 'tippler' and disgorging its load onto shaking screens (driven by the powered shaft on the left) which sort the coal into three different sizes, the larger coal traversing picking belts leading into railway wagons below.
(C.M.Percy, 'The Mechanical Equipment of Collieries', (Manchester, 1905), p.629).

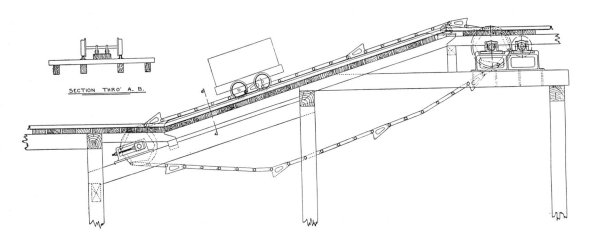

SECTION THRO' A. B.

The tram circuit was carefully graded to allow narrow-gauge railway trucks to move under gravity from the shaft-head over a weighing machine and tippler. However, it was normally necessary to incorporate in the circuit a 'creeper' or other device for returning trams to the shaft-head level. Trams ran by gravity to the foot of the creeper; projecting lugs on a powered endless chain engaged the leading axle of each tram and hauled it to the top of the incline.
(C.M.Percy, 'The Mechanical Equipment of Collieries' (Manchester, 1905), p.617)
Pictured opposite is the tram creeper at Blaenserchan Colliery.

An extension of the tram circuit at Six Bells Colliery took in the stockyard. Narrow-gauge colliery railways transported materials such as pit props, machinery and rails, between stockyard and pit. Single trams could be pushed short distances by hand. (Opposite): Carefully blended coal was ideally stored in loading bunkers, as shown here at Oakdale Colliery. At collieries where output was delivered direct to an electricity-generating power-station, one or sometimes two dedicated trains of hopper wagons each day would collect the coal. The loading was carried out on the move, the train passing slowly beneath the bunkers, whilst at the power station the wagons were emptied through bottom-opening doors, also carried out without stopping. These were termed 'merry-go-round' trains, and the whole operation was continuous; a train of several hundred tonnes was loaded at the colliery and unloaded at its destination automatically with the minimum of labour. This process is still used at Betws, Tower and Point of Ayr Collieries.

Details of part of the froth-flotation equipment at Taff Merthyr Colliery, showing an electrically driven vertical agitator (top) and a set of rotating horizontal paddles (bottom) for skimming the coal froth from the water surface. The froth is then passed to rotating vacuum drums for recovery of the coal in the form of a dried cake.

(Opposite): The heart of a coal washery is the washbox, in this case a Baum Jig at Oakdale Colliery. Dirty coal and water entered at one end and passed through a series of large tanks where artificial gravity was produced by pulsator air pumps. Coal and waste were suspended at different levels and the shale could be removed by bucket elevators for further treatment, while washed coal of all sizes passed out of the box and on to the next processing stage of screening or grading.

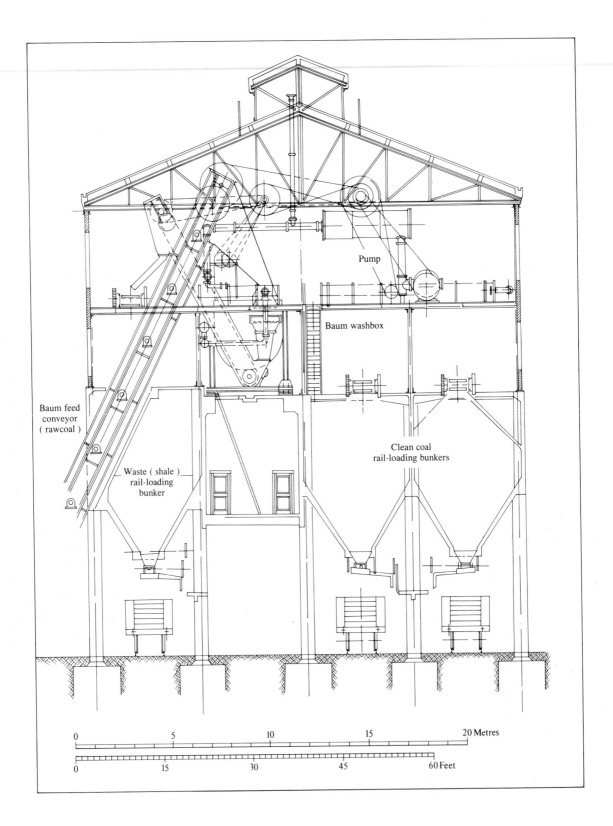

Pump

Baum washbox

Baum feed
conveyor
(rawcoal)

Clean coal
rail-loading bunkers

Waste (shale)
rail-loading
bunker

| 0 | | 5 | | 10 | | 15 | | 20 Metres |

| 0 | | 15 | | 30 | | 45 | | 60 Feet |

Washing has to be a continuous process as conveyors and machines full of coal and shale slurry cannot be stopped and started. If there are areas where a build up of material is likely, then provision is made for diverting some of the excess back to an earlier stage in the system. Vibrating screens, sufficient water and scraper conveyors are employed to ensure that there is no blockage, whatever the material being handled. Output from a vibrating screen (upper left) is transferred to another (lower right) via a chute from which larger particles are removed by a bucket elevator (Merthyr Vale Colliery)
(Opposite): Sectional drawing dating from 1934 of the washery erected at Penallta Colliery. Coal was lifted by conveyor, on the left, to the top of the building and processed on its way down to the railway trucks at ground level.
(British Coal drawings, Glamorgan Archives Service)

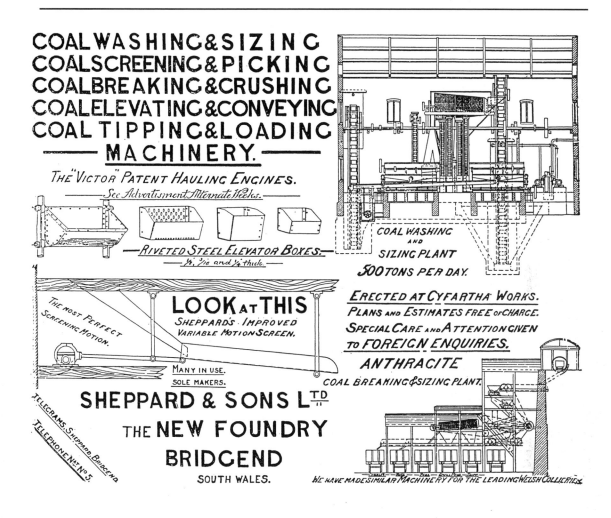

COAL WASHING & SIZING
COAL SCREENING & PICKING
COAL BREAKING & CRUSHING
COAL ELEVATING & CONVEYING
COAL TIPPING & LOADING
MACHINERY.

THE "VICTOR" PATENT HAULING ENGINES.
See Advertisement Alternate Weeks.

RIVETED STEEL ELEVATOR BOXES.
⅛, ³⁄₁₆ and ¼ thick.

THE MOST PERFECT SCREENING MOTION.

LOOK AT THIS
SHEPPARD'S IMPROVED VARIABLE MOTION SCREEN.

MANY IN USE.
SOLE MAKERS.

COAL WASHING
AND
SIZING PLANT
500 TONS PER DAY.

ERECTED AT CYFARTHA WORKS.
PLANS AND ESTIMATES FREE OF CHARGE.
SPECIAL CARE AND ATTENTION GIVEN
TO FOREIGN ENQUIRIES.
ANTHRACITE
COAL BREAKING & SIZING PLANT.

SHEPPARD & SONS LTD
THE NEW FOUNDRY
BRIDGEND
SOUTH WALES.

TELEGRAMS, SHEPPARD, BRIDGEND.
TELEPHONE N.º Nº 5.

WE HAVE MADE SIMILAR MACHINERY FOR THE LEADING WELSH COLLIERIES.

Advertisement for coal preparation and washing equipment from Sheppard & Sons of Bridgend in 1900. It was possible to buy anything from a washer to a washery from any of the colliery suppliers at this time; specialization was not as common as today and competition must have been fierce. ('The Colliery Guardian', 1900).

(Opposite): Various large cones were a common, if mystifying feature, of many colliery sites. Many large cones were simple water-filtration devices with impurities sliding to the base. This is the base of a smaller Chance sand-cone separator (at Onllwyn Washery) showing the inlet pipes supplying water at different levels to hold the sand in suspension, creating a specific gravity between that of coal and shale; when dirty coal is introduced at the top, the clean coal rises and the shale sinks.

FIG. I.

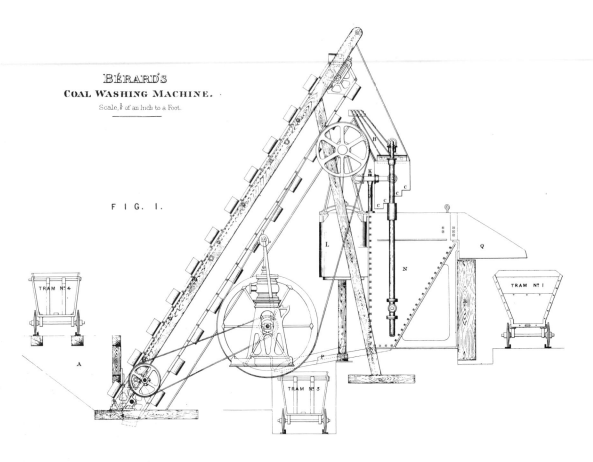

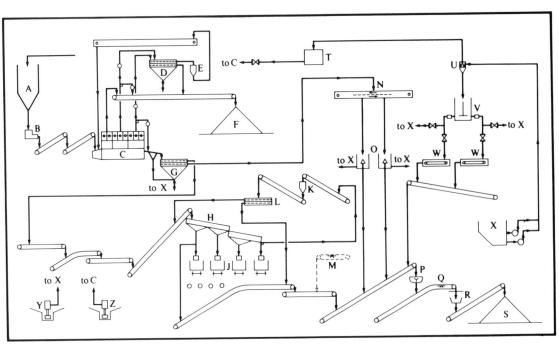

(Above): There are two basic variants of the vibrating screen in a modern washery: one is a de-watering screen that agitates the coal as it travels over a very fine metal screen through which only water will pass, and the other simply grades large quantities of coal passing over a vibrating mesh. The clean coal screens shown here at the Taff Merthyr coal-preparation plant take the washed output from the Baum jig and sort it into three sizes: small coal (less than $^1/_2$ in. (12.5mm.)) passes straight out for further treatment and blending, medium (2in. x $^1/_2$ in. (50 x 12.5mm.)) passes through the screen and is conveyed to the blending storage bunker, and large coal (5in. x 2in. (125 x 50mm)) falls down the chutes at the end into a coal crusher before transfer to the blending bunker.

(Opposite,top): Drawing of an early coal-washing machine installed at a colliery in Ebbw Vale in 1865. Such machines were the precursors of the more sophisticated and highly successful Baum jig and used the principle that shale and coal have different specific gravities. Water is forced up through a tank containing the dirty coal, the shale sinks and the coal rises allowing both to be removed mechanically. ('Proceedings of the South Wales Institute of Engineers', 27 Aug.1869).

(Opposite,below): Deep Navigation Colliery. Schematic layout of washery. Modern washeries are centrally controlled and the operator sits at a remote console in front of a display plan fitted with switches and illuminated sections. Additional monitoring of the processes is by closed-circuit television cameras, and the manager has the ability to shut down parts of the plant, redirect flow, or alter the speed of processing according to the supply of coal from the pit. The washing system is designed to cope with the maximum output of the mine and if a breakdown occurs, surge bunkers and stockpiles are provided to store run-of-mine coal for later treatment so as not to disrupt underground production.

The architecturally nondescript exteriors of washery buildings (as here at Oakdale Colliery) concealed the importance of the coal-prepartion plant and washery to the colliery. Construction was substantial, to withstand the effects of the continual vibration of heavy machinery inside, and consisted of heavy steel joist framing with brick infill. More modern structures were similarly framed, although clad in the ubiquitous corrugated steel sheeting.

(Opposite): As a consequence of the Aberfan tip disaster in 1966, greater attention is now paid to the safe disposal of shale waste from mining operations. Not only are the sites for tipping carefully chosen and prepared, but the waste itself is treated to increase its stability in modern slurry plants, such as this plant (Oakdale Colliery) that had been added to earlier washeries. Shale sizes are blended, in a similar way to the coal, and moisture content is carefully controlled. These functionally important structures are yet more anonymous sheds with corrugated cladding at the coal preparation plants.

Workshops and Stores

Workshops for the maintenance of colliery equipment must already have been part of the infrastructure of the larger collieries of south-west Wales from the eighteenth century. Smithies and carpentry workplaces appeared on valuations of Swansea Valley collieries from the early nineteenth century; Graigola Colliery in 1831 had two smithies (with a store of spare tramplates) and a sawpit 'made with oak poles'.[1]

In 1840 the buildings at the mouth of another mining tunnel in the Swansea Valley were mapped and show a group of five structures (some of which survive) serving seven different functions at 'Tŷ-mawr Level' or 'Lefel Fawr' in Abercrâf.[2] One long building was subdivided into the 'carpenter's shop' and 'forge'- these were the two main elements of the workshops in the first decades of the nineteenth century, and later an electrician's shop was generally added. A second range at Abercrâf was that of the 'storehouse'; the forerunner of the later colliery stores. As the size and sophistication of collieries increased in the nineteenth and twentieth centuries so did the number of functional buildings designed to serve specialist purposes. Subsidiary buildings often also included fitting-shops, sawmills, locomotive sheds and stables.

The twin range of the Oakdale Navigation Company's colliery workshops of 1908 (illustrated), with their central pediment, were fairly typical in size for their date. Their surface ornament reflected that of the other contemporary buildings of this substantial and adequately capitalized concern (the Oakdale Company was a subsidiary of the large 'Tredegar Iron & Coal Company').

The colliery blacksmiths' shops had distinctive long rows of tall chimneys (see the earlier photograph of Blaenserchan), each chimney venting one of the multiple smithy hearths in the building below.

In the late nineteenth and twentieth centuries

(Opposite): A scene typical of the colliery workshops were the lines of smithy hearths with their typical 'beehive' brick smoke-hoods leading to distinctive tall chimneys extending above the edge of the workshop's roof. This example was at South Celynen.

colliery workshops had acquired a greatly increased capacity for machining parts. The photograph shows part of the long interior of the Deep Navigation Colliery fitting shops. These were probably converted from a heightened stable block in the 1940s, and like many such installations was stocked with second-hand machinery, probably War Office surplus equipment. A multitude of such machines stood under a travelling crane, with a branch of the colliery's 2ft. 5in. (0.74 m.) gauge railway running between the machinery. Reference to the plan made by the Royal Commission in March 1991, just before Deep Navigation's closure, shows the range of machinery deployed in such a building. On the photograph, taken from a mid-point in the building looking southwards, the radial-arm drill of 1939 (14 on the plan) is visible to the right of the railway line with workbenches against the wall on the right of the photograph. To the left of the railway line, and opposite the radial drill, is a 'Startrite' H250M band-saw (13 on the plan). Against the wall at the extreme left of the photograph is a pillar drill (12 on the plan), and the machine set against the window to the right is a 'Monarch' lathe (11 on the plan), made in the United States in 1940. The north-western elevation of this long narrow range presented a white-rendered facade towards the rest of the colliery; the building abutting the old colliery stores to the south. The stripping of the corrugated-iron cladding of the rear of this building at demolition revealed its lower structure to have been similar to that of the adjacent stores: its walls were of Pennant sandstone rubble with ashlar in similar stone acting as a dressing around all the openings and for the quoining. The upper small openings had dressings of yellow brick. A line of five tall stacks indicated where the smithy hearths had been - three remained in use until closure.

In the building were also five small enclosed areas: one served as the office for the fitting-shop, two served as store-rooms, one was the pitman's cabin and the fifth was the fire station.

Workshops were also sometimes constructed underground, as in the case of the 'fitter's cabin', built into a blocked-up roadway at Big Pit, Blaenavon.

References

1. '1831 - estimate of all the materials at Graigola colliery taken the 8th June and following days as hereunder stated', William Kirkhouse's Letter Book, Swansea Central Library M.S. 466.

2. Shown on the deposited plan (no.77) of the Swansea Vale Railway, Glamorgan Archives Service, Quarter Sessions Records.

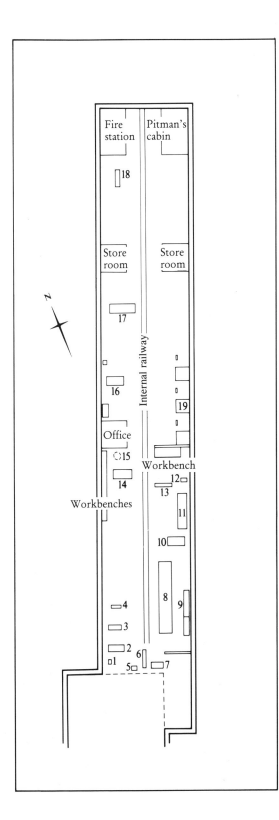

Items of Machinery in the Fitting Shop of Deep Navigation Colliery (March 1991).

1. 'Union' Pedestal Grinder, made by John Hall (Tools) Ltd., machine tool specialists of Birmingham and Bristol;
2. Slotter (for cutting key-ways in couplings), made by Ormerod Shapers Ltd., Hebden Bridge, England;
3. Lathe, made by the Colchester Lathe Co. Ltd.;
4. Shaper (185), made by Elliot in England (never wired-up for use at Deep Navigation Colliery);
5. 'Union' Pedestal Grinder, made by John Hall (Tools) Ltd., machine tool specialists of Birmingham and Bristol;
6. Shaper (Type 6MR), made by Invicta in England;
7. Power Pack (for testing hydraulic equipment), Gullick;
8. Lathe (Taylor Multiple disk clutch), made by the British Thomson-Houston Co Ltd., Rugby, England;
9. Switch Gear (electrical), never used;
10. Vertical Milling Machine, made by Jarocinska Fabryka Obrabiarek, Poland;
11. Lathe, made by The Monarch Machine Tool Co., Sidney, Ohio, U.S.A., dated 9-1940;
12. Pillar Drill (small), made by F. O'Brien & Co. Ltd., Swadlincote, Burton-on-Trent, England;
13. Band Saw (H250M), 'Startrite';
14. Radial Arm Drill, made by William Asquith, Halifax, England, dated 25.7.39;
15. Brazier;
16. Steam Hammer (latterly operated by compressed air), B & S Massey Steam Hammer Makers & Patentees, Openshaw, Manchester, England;
17. Guillotine and Punch, made by De Bergue Machine Tools Ltd., Manchester, England;
18. Profile Cutter, maker unknown.

The fitting shop that was in use at the time of the closure of Deep Navigation Colliery in the Spring of 1991 was probably a converted nineteenth-century stables . Rather typically it was stocked with surplus equipment from World War II and from other closed collieries. The overhead crane and the internal railway were both used for the movement of machines and materials in the workshop.

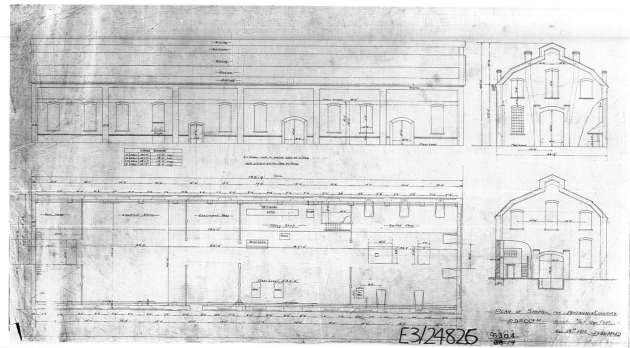

E3/24826

PLAN OF SHOPS FOR BRITANNIA COLLIERY
P.D.S.Co Ltd   Scale 1/16" One Foot
Oct 19th 1910

134

(Above): Small subsidiary workshops were common, this workshop was underground at Big Pit.

(Opposite,top): Design drawing for the workshops at Britannia Colliery (1910-14) showing the multiple chimneys for the smithy hearths. (British Coal drawings, Glamorgan Archives Service)

(Opposite,bottom): Top-lit double workshops building at Oakdale Colliery (1908-10).

Colliery Offices

The colliery manager must always have needed space to plan and work on the adminstration, finances and engineering of the colliery under his supervision. Early offices survive of the 'Tŷ-mawr Level' or 'Lefel Fawr' Colliery at the head of the Swansea Valley. This colliery was built in 1805 by the 'Abercrave Colliery Company', owned by Daniel Harper, with a colliery heading (tunnel) driven over a mile (1.6km.) underground.[1] The block of buildings housing the colliery manager's house and his separate office had their respective functions recorded on a plan of 1840.[2] There seems to have been a fair provision of room, equivalent to a contemporary dwelling-house of the period, with a single room on the ground floor, and two on the first, all with fireplaces.

The surviving plans of the Edwardian pit at Penallta show the relatively generous provision of offices in a large colliery at the heyday of the south Wales coal industry. By 1931 the total workforce of the pit had reached 3,208, and viewed from that perspective the office provision may seem very modest by today's standards. The manager's office lay between two wings on a 'C' shaped plan; one arm of the accommodation was occupied by clerks concerned with accounts and administration, and the other by those working in engineering - the engineer, with his surveyors and draughtsmen. The manager's office was some 16ft. by 20ft. (4.87m. by 6.09 m.) with two large windows, a bathroom, and a toilet; the engineer's office was some 16ft. by 18ft. (4.87 m.by 5.48 m.) with one large window, but without a bathroom or toilet. The manager also had the use of an adjacent, interconnected spare room. Other staff were in shared accommodation. The clerks had two rooms, with a toilet in between, and separate small rooms for a telephone and for stores. The draughtsmen had a large room interconnected with the engineer's office,

beyond which was a toilet and then the surveyors' large room with a 'safe' vault attached. This latter was a small room enclosed by 2ft. (0.61m.) thick walls and with a ceiling 1ft. 6in. (0.46m.) thick. The differences of level on which the office was sited, as with so many Welsh buildings, allowed the insertion of a basement, here sited below the clerks' room. As at many Powell Duffryn colliery offices, metal braces carried a canopy running along the front of the clerks' room allowing miners some shelter while awaiting payment through the hole cut in the base of one of the windows.

A substantial porch gave access to the Penallta Colliery office building. Illustrated is the ruined 'shell' porch, that gave some pretension to the Llantrisant Colliery office, again a large colliery of the early twentieth century. Post-nationalization (1947) design was far more utilitarian, as illustrated by the pay offices block at Six Bells Colliery. A variety of office accommodation housed the various administrative staffs of the collieries with the 'dirty' or pit-top offices and the 'clean' or manager's office.

However, many office staff and management occupied various buildings that had been added and adapted as the colliery had developed. At Deep Navigation the original offices became the local boys' club and the later offices occupied the former baths building.

References

1   Public Record Office, Kew. General Assembly Minutes of the Swansea Canal Company, 1794 - 1822, 2 July 1805, W.G.Thomas, 'Industrial Archaeology of the Upper Swansea Valley', *Brycheiniog* XIV (1970), pp.69-70.
2   Glamorgan Archives Service, Quarter Sessions records deposited plan of the Swansea Vale Railway (No. 77), May 1840.

(Opposite): Colliery offices were the centre of operations of very large workforces of several hundred or even thousands of people. Yet they were low technology, often homely, places. In this photograph, Glyn Morgan, the last manager of Big Pit, Blaenavon, is pictured in his office November 1980.

(Above): The 'shell' porch to the now ruined offices of the early twentieth-century Llantrisant Colliery gave the building some pretension. (Below): The design drawings for the Edwardian Colliery Office at Penallta (1906-09) shows a structure from which no less than 3,208 miners were directed by 1931.

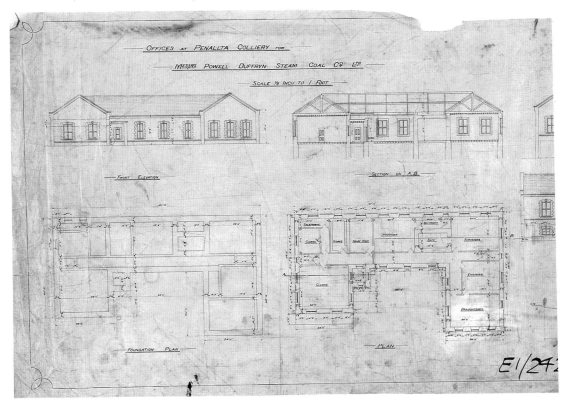

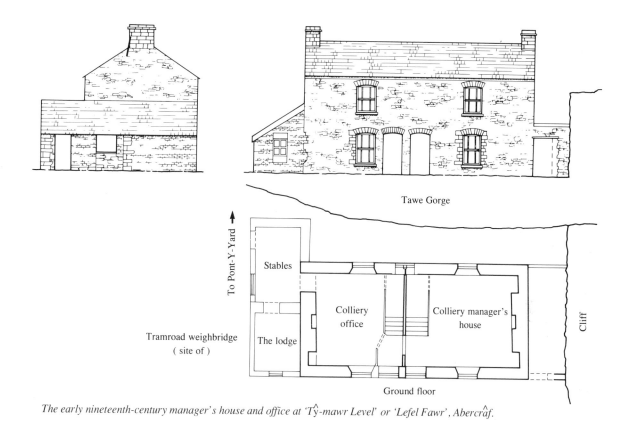

Tawe Gorge

To Pont-Y-Yard

Stables

Colliery office

Colliery manager's house

Cliff

The lodge

Tramroad weighbridge
(site of)

Ground floor

The early nineteenth-century manager's house and office at 'Tŷ-mawr Level' or 'Lefel Fawr', Abercrâf.

National Coal Board modern functionalism as applied to its Pay Office at Six Bells Colliery

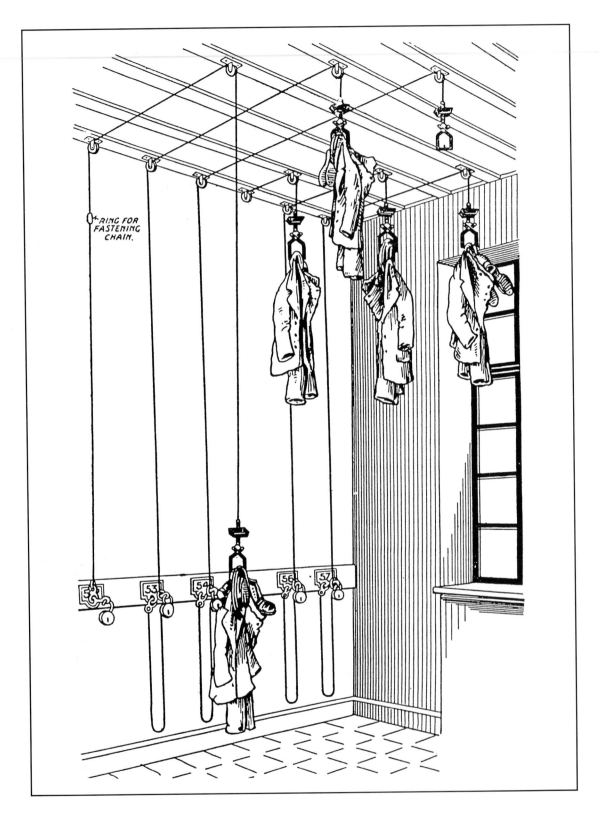

RING FOR
FASTENING
CHAIN.

Pithead Baths

Although pithead baths were available to miners in Germany, France and Belgium from about 1880, and were in common use there by the beginning of the twentieth century, British colliery owners were notably reluctant to provide these facilities until required by legislation in 1911.

In Britain arguments both for and against the provision of washing and drying facilities were advanced by, amongst others, the medical profession, miners' federations, colliery owners and politicians. It was generally recognized that the life of the average miner's wife was one of continual drudgery, and a constant battle against coal grime.

There were some pithead baths built in Britain prior to the 1911 Act; those opened in 1908 at Stanley Colliery in Derbyshire were among the earliest. Facilities there included a swimming pool, several plunge baths and a shower bath. The scheme was carried out by workmen from the colliery company and cost £260. These baths were open only from the beginning of April to mid-October each year. In a reply to a parliamentary enquiry, the colliery manager stated that, '*The men appreciated the baths, but they did not come to bath immediately they came out of the pit. Indeed, very few took a bath before they left the colliery premises. They prefer to go home, wash and change themselves, have their dinners, a smoke and a rest, and then come back in large numbers to take advantage of the swimming and washing baths.*' He also felt that because of some difficulty in providing adequate hot water at some pits, the Act should only take effect at new collieries opened after the passing of the Bill. Summing up his account he said, '*From my experience of miners I am certain they will resent being compelled to take baths immediately they come out of the pit, and if the clause is adopted it is sure to give trouble.*'[1]

Henry Davies, Director of Mining Instruction to Glamorgan County Council, was a vigorous campaigner for the introduction of washing facilities

at all mines. In 1911 he published a pamphlet on the benefits of using pithead baths.

Sections 77 and 86 of the Coal Mines Act of 1911 made provision to allow washing and drying accommodation at collieries. Regulations would not take effect at any mine until a two-thirds majority of the workmen affected, i.e. underground workers and those engaged on the surface in handling coal, agreed to ask for the facilities to be installed and undertook to pay half the maintenance costs. The amount of money available under the Act was 3d. per head per week to meet expenses, including 5 per cent. per annum to the owner of the mine on the capital outlay.

It was considered unnecessary to lay down different requirements for different classes of mines, but recommended that, so long as there was no loss of efficiency, modifications of the regulations might be allowed in particular cases. Certain classes of mines were exempt, such as mines where the total number of workmen affected was less than 100, mines held on a lease with less than 10 years to run, and mines which, in the opinion of the Secretary of State, would be worked out within 10 years.

The first colliery in Britain to have the recommended washing facilities, as set out in the 1911 Act, was at Atherton in Lancashire. These baths were opened at the end of 1915 and were described as a 'model installation'. The shower or spray bath was not the original form of pithead bath. At first, in Germany, plunge baths were used but it was found that contagious diseases, particularly of the eye, were communicated. The Government ordered the substitution of the shower bath.[2]

In June 1913, David Davies M.P., proprietor of the Ocean Coal Company, sent a delegation of men from his collieries to inspect baths facilities on the Continent. Their observations and reports led to the installation of pithead baths at the company's mines, and in June 1916 the earliest baths in Wales were opened at Deep Navigation Colliery. They were designed and built by G.D. Jones, the colliery engineer, and were based on the French system, with single shower cubicles directly communicating with a large central dressing and drying hall.

The dressing room was fitted with 800 chains for raising and suspending the miners' clothes in the roof space above a system of radiators. In a side corridor were 54 adult cubicles constructed of white glazed brick, divided by T-shaped walls, and at one end of the main hall was a room containing 16 cubicles for boys under 17 years of age, making a total of 70 baths for workmen. A separate chamber containing five baths was set aside for officials, with lockers for their clothing instead of the hanging system used in the main baths. Toilets, an 'ambulance room' equipped with first-aid facilities, and various offices completed the layout of the building. This distinctive building, with its high central hall and 'aisles', was later converted into offices and replaced by a new bath-house, built to the British plan with conventional lockers to replace the high roof hangers used for storing clothes in the continental system. The later building was in the modernist style that signified the work of the Miners' Welfare Committee architectural team.

Workmen were charged 6d. per week for the use of the bath-house to cover any working expenses, including costs for heating the water, supervisors' wages, and washing down of the shower rooms. Any surplus collected was handed over to the workmen's committee, to be disposed of as they saw fit. The total cost of building was £8,000; approximately £6,500 was donated by the wife of David Davies as a gift to the miners of Treharris. Mrs Davies also presented towels and soap to the first thousand people who used the baths.

The surviving baths at Penallta Colliery were built by the Miners' Welfare Committee in 1938 to provide facilities for 2,016 men. The brown-brick building is in the Welfare Committee's distinctive modernist style, with a deep bay window and the entrance having the typical vertical banding of brick headers to either side, multiple string-courses and multi-pane metal-framed windows. The showers were on two floors, with two drying lockers per miner for their working and clean clothes. The building also included a canteen and medical centre which formed several irregular stepped wings arranged around a central well for light.

References

1   The Colliery Guardian, 28 April 1911, p.851
2   The Colliery Guardian, 16 February 1912, pp.325 - 326

(Opposite, top): Plan of the early (1916) bath-house at Deep Navigation Colliery showing the central dressing room above which 800 chains suspended the miners' clothes. The integral colliery offices eventually expanded to fill the whole block. (Opposite, below): The original bath-house at Deep Navigation Colliery was designed by the colliery engineer, G.D.Jones, and followed earlier Continental European design in having a high clerestory into which the miners' clothes could be hoisted.

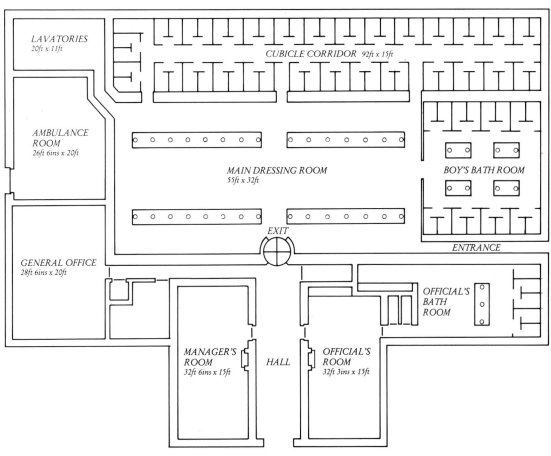

LAVATORIES
20ft x 11ft

CUBICLE CORRIDOR 92ft x 15ft

AMBULANCE
ROOM
26ft 6ins x 20ft

MAIN DRESSING ROOM
55ft x 32ft

BOY'S BATH ROOM

GENERAL OFFICE
28ft 6ins x 20ft

EXIT

ENTRANCE

OFFICIAL'S
BATH
ROOM

MANAGER'S
ROOM
32ft 6ins x 15ft

HALL

OFFICIAL'S
ROOM
32ft 3ins x 15ft

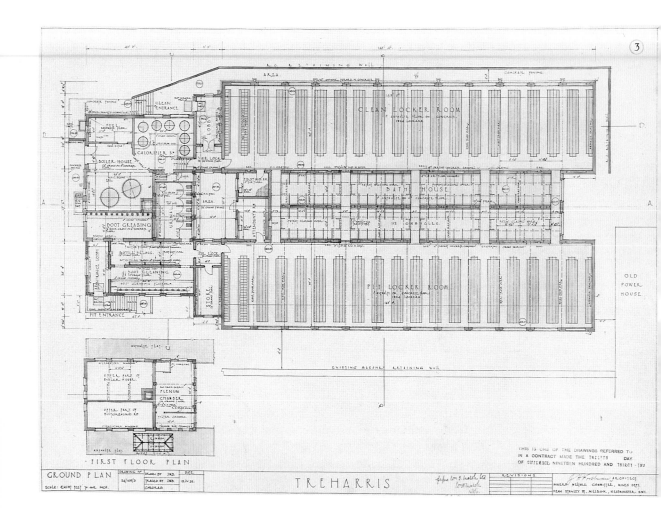

(Above): The later baths at Deep Navigation Colliery were built in 1932 and followed the traditional British tripartite plan of having pit, or dirty, lockers on one side, showers in the centre and clean lockers along the other side. First-aid, or 'ambulance' rooms formed part of both the 1916 and 1932 baths, but the later baths also had the amenities of bottle-filling, and boot-greasing, rooms.

(Opposite, top): Distinctive colliery baths were built by the Miners' Welfare Committee on a large scale in the international modernist style and were in marked contrast to the traditional architecture of the earlier colliery buildings on the pit sites to which they were added.

(Opposite, below): Multiple bathing cubicles in the bath house at Six Bells Colliery.

144

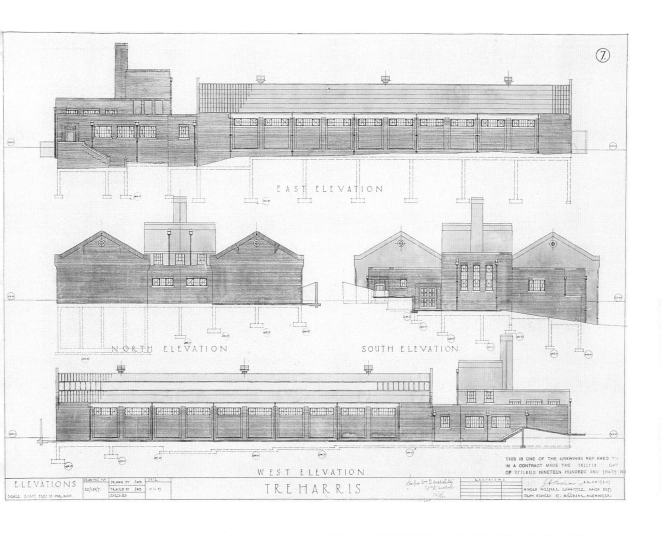

EAST ELEVATION

NORTH ELEVATION

SOUTH ELEVATION

WEST ELEVATION

TREHARRIS

THIS IS ONE OF THE DRAWINGS REFERRED TO
IN A CONTRACT MADE THE TWELFTH DAY
OF SEPTEMBER, NINETEEN HUNDRED AND THIRTY TWO

ELEVATIONS

SCALE EIGHT FEET TO ONE INCH

Conclusion

This examination of the architectural and engineering features accompanying the coalmining process has not made it possible to define any pithead complex as a typical 'Welsh Colliery'.

By contrast, there were characteristically Welsh industrial and social landscapes dependent on the great steam-coal trade. These made the south Wales valleys a distinctive area with great hillside rows of housing punctuated by chapels and Miners' Institutes. A similar infrastructure developed in north-east Wales in less linear settlements, as at Bagillt, Brymbo, Mostyn and Rhosllanerchrugog.

The relative impact of the industry on the two regions can be quantified by the numbers employed in

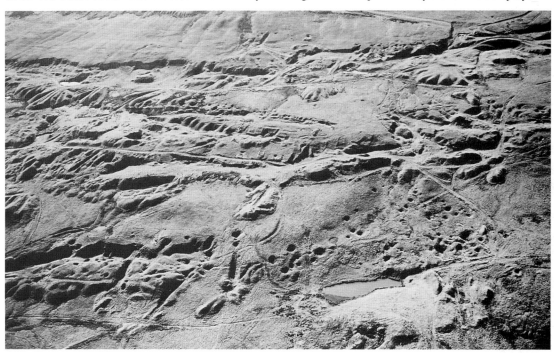

(Above): The world's largest ironworks of the early nineteenth century were based on the shallow coal and iron reserves available on the northern rim of the south Wales coalfield. The landscape patterns produced by this outcrop working are now disappearing with the rapid progress of both land reclamation and opencast mining of the small reserves. From the late eighteenth century onwards, much of the coal for the Cyfarthfa Ironworks at Merthyr Tydfil was obtained from seams exposed on the north-eastern slope of Mynydd Aberdâr. This aerial view looking towards the south-west shows part of the workings. Below the crest of the ridge, at the top of the photograph, four main coal outcrops have been exploited; from top to bottom these are: the nine feet seam, the middle coal measures, the lower coal measures (above and below the track running across the centre of the photograph from the left), and the Garw vein in the lower coal measures. The long depression in the left middle distance, just below the track and above the Garw workings, is an ironstone level. Further ironstone levels lie in the lower right of the photograph.

(Opposite): This aerial view shows early mineral workings north of Brynmawr at Clydach Terraces looking south-eastwards towards the Heads of the Valleys road which runs across the photograph from the top-left corner. In the foreground are early ironstone workings with, nearer the Heads of the Valleys road, a mixture of ironstone and coal workings. The crescent-shaped trench between the two is the remains of early open mining along a five-feet coal seam. Note the advancing border of the reclaimed land to the right and, above, the Heads of the Valleys road descending into the Clydach Gorge.

Long terraces lined the hillsides above the valley-bottom pits of south Wales, and were often built by and named after colliery owners. Distinguished by large windows and gardens, they offered better accommodation than that available at comparable rent in contemporary large towns. This view is of the Lower, Middle and Upper terraces of Stanleytown in the Rhondda Fach. The school at the far end of Upper Terrace is boarded up while the public house and adjoining mission at the near end have been demolished. Also gone is the Cynllwyn-du Colliery (1858) in the valley bottom and modern amenity buildings can be seen on the site of the colliery sidings. In the distance is the large tip characteristically placed on the lip of the valley (by 1914) after all the available land along the river bank was covered in spoil in the Victorian and Edwardian periods. A second powered-incline later also hauled waste up from the Ferndale Colliery to the north, the site of a firedamp explosion which killed 178 men and boys on 8 November 1867.

the Edwardian heyday of coal mining in 1911 when 214,000 were employed in the industry in south Wales as against 14,500 in the old north-eastern counties of Denbighshire and Flintshire. That the transformation of society in south Wales was a Victorian phenomenon can be recognized when it is considered that south Wales had only 11,000 coalminers in 1841, relatively not that much greater than the 3,700 then employed in north-east Wales.[1] South Wales, in the boom time of 'King Coal', between 1901 and 1911, absorbed immigrants at a faster relative rate than anywhere in the world apart from the U.S.A.: 129,000 people

The ever-present danger of the mines helps to explain the widespread religious faith of the mining communities. The enginehouse-like facade of Capel Seion (1870, first chapel 1846) at Morriston was built by Baptists who first founded a congregation among the colliers and copper-workers of this planned town in 1809.

moved into the area. In fact, between 1851 and 1911 a total of 366,000 people had migrated to Carmarthenshire, Glamorgan and Monmouthshire. This profoundly affected the nature of the Welsh population for in 1801 only 20 per cent. of the population of Wales lived in Glamorgan and Monmouthshire, but by 1911 nearly 63 per cent. were resident in these two counties. In the period 1851-1911 the population of the two north-eastern counties of Denbighshire and Flintshire had also approximately doubled.

The linguistic balance of Wales was greatly altered by the need of the booming coal industry for labour. Before the 1890s the majority of the people arriving to work in south Wales had come from the more rural counties to the north but by the beginning of the twentieth century migrant workers might equally come from Gloucestershire and Somerset; it was a change that had deep cultural effects on south-east Wales.[2]

The hard and dangerous nature of mining helped to weld the valley communities closely together. In 1851 64 per cent of the population of Merthyr Tydfil went to religious services; in Pontypool it was 74 per cent. The average for England and Wales was only 36 per cent. The deep religious nature of this society was reflected in the intensity of chapel construction. By 1905 there were about 800 Nonconformist chapels in the valleys area of south Wales. In the Rhondda alone there were 150 chapels at this time. The massive pediments of these great enginehouse-like buildings dominate the Welsh mining towns. However, with disuse and demolition, these manifestations of the faith of the mining people may fade, like the collieries themselves which were the economic focus of the mining communities and like the Institutes that once provided a social base for the area.[3]

The Workmen's or Miners' Institutes were also very large communal structures characteristic of the

The secular communal life of the miners was centred around Miners' Institutes such as this example built at Rhosllanerchrugog in the north-east Wales coalfield. They were paid for from voluntary donations by the colliery workers. (Pat Frost)

mining communities; those at Abercynon, Blaenavon and Parc and Dare resembling music halls or theatres. They were paid for by the workers themselves with the voluntary deduction of a penny in the pound from their wages. Nixon's Workmen's Institute at Mountain Ash, designed by Dan Lloyd in 1899, is one of the most elaborate. Its terracotta facade fronted a multi-purpose structure that included a gymnasium, library, swimming pool and theatre. The smaller Miner's Institute from the mining village of Oakdale has now been moved to the Welsh Folk Museum at St. Fagans. Some, such as the Institute at Blaenavon, have been

refurbished, but the future of many is in doubt and several doubtless will be demolished.

In size and layout the architecture of the collieries themselves was more diverse than the relatively simple communal structures of the chapels and institutes. They varied from the large collections of disparate structures characteristic of the south Wales, north-east Wales and every other large British coalfield, through the cathedral-like engine halls of the Edwardian height of the industry at Penallta or Britannia, to the grandiose overall planning apparent from 1947 with the dawn of nationalization, as seen at Maerdy. More modest were

The chapel-building enthusiasm of the coal-mining and coal-fuelled metallurgical communities culminated in a building boom between 1870 and 1910, paralleling the steam-coal boom itself. Pictured above is the 'Cathedral of Welsh Nonconformity', John Humphreys' Tabernacle at Morriston, built in 1872 in an unique mixture of Classical, Romanesque and Gothic styles.

the huts and assemblages often found among the rural coalmining industries of Pembrokeshire and Anglesey.[4]

The Welsh coalfields will continue to retain a number of colliery museums and conserved sites. These include a growing number of consolidated eighteenth- and nineteenth-century beam-engine houses with statutory protection and public access, such as Scott's Pit of 1817-19 at Swansea and Grove Colliery of 1856 at Stepaside in Pembrokeshire. The former includes the excavated bases of ancillary structures. Later colliery complexes are open to visitors at Lewis Merthyr Colliery ('The Rhondda Heritage Park'); Cefn Coed Colliery Museum , Crynant, and Big Pit at Blaenavon; the last has visitor access to some of its underground roadways. Unfortunately, certain ancillary functions at these museums have been lost:

the pithead baths at Lewis Merthyr Colliery, and the washery at Big Pit have been demolished. The visitor looking for more complete colliery complexes will have to wander further afield in Britain: to Caphouse Colliery Museum in Yorkshire or to the Scottish Mining Museum (minus its underground component).

By contrast awesome steam machines can attract popular interest and attention when other elements of coalmining largely disappear without trace. Solitary surviving engine houses, to be exhibited with steam winding-engines, include the Elliot East Pit engine house of 1891 in the Rhymney Valley, the Hetty shaft engine house (and headframe) near the Rhondda Heritage Park, and the Bersham Colliery engine house (with the former Point of Ayr Colliery winder to be placed in or alongside) and headframe, near Wrexham.

Collieries in the first half of the twentieth century began to acquire buildings specifically catering for the welfare of their workers: baths, canteens and first-aid stations. Pictured above is a scene at the opening of the Morlais Colliery canteen in the 1940s with the colliery owner Sir Evan Williams (at centre, in bow tie) about to make a presentation. (Anne Morris)

A Morlais Colliery engine, engine house, and head-frame has been re-erected at the Kidwelly Industrial Museum and another engine from Morlais can be seen at Cefn Coed Colliery Museum. Collections of other large colliery steam-engines (listed in the Appendix) can be seen at the Welsh Industrial and Maritime Museum in Cardiff and at the South Wales Miners Museum at Afan Argoed. Importantly, these Museums both have extensive collections dealing with the life of the miners, as does the South Wales Miners Library in Swansea, which has a large collection of miners' union banners.

Not all collieries can be kept as museums. However, they did constitute a large stock of buildings - some of them suitable to be converted to new uses. Other coalmining areas of Europe have witnessed a

similar scale of colliery closure, and possibilities for the future alternative reuse and retention of some of the colliery buildings in Wales may be considered by comparison with the Ruhr Coalfield in Germany.

One large Ruhr colliery, 'Waltrop I/II', with massive engine-halls and buildings erected in Imperial Prussian Gothic in 1903-06, is being refurbished after lying derelict for several years, so that it can be reused for industrial and office space. The large engine-hall and workshops of Penallta Colliery in south Wales are of similar age and are now protected as 'listed' historic buildings. The elaborate external decoration at Waltrop is paralleled by the polychrome brickwork of the fine buildings of Crumlin Navigation Colliery (Lower Ebbw Valley), built in 1907-11 and closed in 1967-68. The structures were listed as historic buildings upon closure and both winding-houses are used for storage; the office-block alongside has trees and shrubs sprouting through it; most of the other buildings are reused for garaging. It is hoped that they will be converted to more permanent uses soon. The impressive range of large stone buildings remaining from Llanbradach Colliery in the Rhymney Valley, closed in 1964, now have a variety of light industrial uses. The huge engine-hall of the Llantrisant or Ynysmaerdy Colliery at Llanharan in Mid-Glamorgan stands in abandoned splendour on farmland with the adjoining buildings used for agricultural purposes. Post-war pithead baths at Bersham near Wrexham have been converted to workshops and small industrial units as a business park.

This succession of *ad hoc* conversions contrasts with the Walthrop I/II and Zollverein 12 Pits where conversion into art galleries, concert rooms and halls and office accommodation continues apace. Much machinery and the vast boiler-house will be preserved *in situ*, with meeting rooms inserted into some of the huge boilers. Schemes of this scale and prestige akin to the conversion of the Albert Dock in Liverpool have not yet been proposed for the colliery complexes of the Welsh coalfields.

Many small colliery buildings have slipped unnoticed into new industrial uses in Wales, but this has not generally happened in the cases of recent colliery closures where comprehensive programmes of clearance and landscaping have generally followed immediately on the cessation of mining.

Ruined remains of earlier Welsh coalmines lie dotted across the landscapes of the coalfields. Some still include machinery and important structural detail, the most important site being the mid-nineteenth-century Glyn Pits at Pontypool. The remains consist of the only rotative beam-engine (of 1845; originally for both pumping and winding) and vertical winding-engine (dating between 1856-65) still *in situ* in the British Isles. The former was cast at the Neath Abbey Ironworks and is supported on a prefabricated iron floor structure typical of the great ironworks era of south Wales (*ca.*1780-1850).[5]

It was coal that established the social structure of modern south Wales and north-east Wales and determined the present population pattern of the country. Coal was central to the economy of Wales and the monuments of its era are reminders of its importance. This book forms a selective introduction to their rich heritage, the survival of which will depend on the continued interest of a population that has now entered a very different industrial age.

Although the days of 'King Coal' have gone, in the more densely populated parts of Wales the legacy of the industry is still with us in the form of the architecture, settlements, archaeology, landscapes and society which this prime extractive industry helped to form and create. The influence of the coal trade on the archaeology of whole landscapes was formerly very apparent. However, with the reclamation of vast tracts of land for other uses, we are now approaching the time when the better preserved of these characteristically Welsh landscapes will have a rarity value.

References

1   A.H.Dodd, *The Industrial Revolution in North Wales*, (Cardiff, 2nd. ed., 1951), p.202.

2   D.Egan, *Coal Society: A History of the South Wales Mining Valleys 1840-1980*, (Llandysul, 1987), pp.71-2.

3   J.B.Hilling, *Cardiff and the Valleys: Architecture and Townscape*, (London, 1973), p.129.

4   T.M.Bassett and Geraint James, 'Coalmining in Anglesey', *Anglesey Antiquarian Society Transactions* (1969-70), pp.137-163.

5   M.Palmer and P.Neaverson, 'The Steam Engines at Glyn Pits Colliery' *Industrial Archaeology Review* XIII.1, (Autumn 1990), pp.7-34; the Neath Abbey Ironworks drawings (West Glamorgan Record Office, Swansea) and the Boulton & Watt Collection (Birmingham Reference Library) contain many drawings of late-eighteenth-and early nineteenth-century south Wales colliery beam-engines and their housings.

Large vertical steam-engines were the preferred machines in use for winding between the 1850s and 1870s. Illustrated on the left of this picture is one of the two large 54in. (1.37 m.) cylinders at the downcast shaft engine house of Deep Navigation Colliery (1872-79 - see exterior photograph on page eight). The engine was suspended over the 32ft. (9.75 m.) winding-drum on an iron frame (visible below the cylinder) and the winding-cables passed through the large opening in the background. The timber-clad machinery in the front of the cylinder contained steam chests and the upright pillars held 14in. (0.36 m.) diameter double beat steam valves. The bells and clock-like winding indicator were for signalling and monitoring the descent and ascent of the cage in what was at the time of construction the deepest shaft in south Wales: 2,280ft. (695 m.) deep. The long horizontal, and short vertical levers on the left hand side are the regulator and brake, while that on the right-hand side was the reverser which controlled the (visible) small steam-cylinder for moving the reversing gear. All the machinery was mirrored on the right hand-side of the enginehouse, outside the frame of the photograph. This impressive engine was replaced by electric motors in 1921-25. The lower drum housing also supported the adjacent headframes and was left in position until the demolition of the colliery in 1991.

Glossary

Glossary of some of the more commonly encountered technical terms

Adit - see *Level.*

Afterdamp - a poisonous and suffocating mixture of gases found underground after a fire or an explosion, consisting of carbon monoxide, carbon dioxide and nitrogen, with very little oxygen.

Air crossing - where one underground *airway* has to cross another without leakage of airflow between the two. Normally, strong side walls and a steel or concrete roof are built in the intake airway creating an airtight bridge. The roof forms the deck of an overbridge carrying the return airway.

Air door - see *Regulator.*

Airway - a tunnel which carries ventilation air; an *intake airway* takes fresh air from the *downcast shaft* and into the workings, while a *return airway* carries stale air towards the *upcast shaft.*

Armoured flexible conveyor or **AFC** - an articulated steel conveyor used in *longwall* mining and able to be slewed over against the coalface as cutting progresses. Transverse bars to drag the mineral are drawn along the top face of the conveyor by motor-driven chains.

Bank - a raised working area around the *shaft* tops; *trams* of coal arriving at the surface could be pushed across the bank and tipped through the *screens* into waiting railway wagons at ground level. On steep valley sides, collieries were set on a series of terraces with the railway tracks at the lowest level.

Banksman - the person responsible for signalling and also loading and unloading the shaft conveyances at the pit *bank.*

Beam-engine - an atmospheric or steam-engine in which the piston rod of the vertical cylinder is attached to one end of a massive, centrally pivoted beam, the other end of which is attached to the plunger rod for operating a pump, or in a *rotative beam-engine,* the crank of a flywheel. In the early nineteenth-century it was commonly used for both pumping and winding.

Bi-cylindro-conical drum - a sophisticated design of winding-drum which has cylindrical sections of different diameter connected by a shallow cone. When a wind starts, maximum torque and minimum speed is required, ideally provided by a small diameter drum. Once inertia is overcome, speed becomes more desirable than torque and a large diameter drum is more appropriate. The bi-cylindro-conical drum fulfils these requirements: the rope starts on the small diameter and as the wind progresses it coils along the cone to reach the full diameter of the cylindrical section.

Blackdamp - a suffocating mine gas consisting mainly of carbon dioxide and nitrogen.

Cage - a frame or lift, generally constructed of steel, with a roof, sides and one or more decks fitted with gates. It is suspended from the winding-rope by a *detaching hook* and runs in guides in the *shaft*; its purpose is to carry men, materials and trams in and out of the mine. A *double-deck cage* gives greater capacity and with two platforms at top and bottom of the shaft allows faster loading and unloading.

Capstan engine (Steam winch) - a small engine geared to lift or haul heavy loads. The *sinking capstan,* used when the *shafts* were being sunk, was generally retained for shaft maintenance and rope changing.

Coal-preparation plant or **CPP** - also known as a washery, the installation where raw coal is cleaned, graded, blended and prepared for the market. The techniques and equipment used have become highly specialized and sophisticated, but broadly coal and dirt have different specific gravities and can be separated in water using one of a wide variety of processes.

Compound engine - a multi-cylinder steam-engine, where the exhaust from one cylinder is introduced to another in order to gain the maximum work from the steam. A *simple engine* uses steam only once to move the piston. Reusing the exhaust once (or twice in a *triple expansion engine*) makes compound engines more powerful and cheaper to run. The primary or high-pressure cylinder exhausts to the secondary, low-pressure one; if they share a common piston rod and are therefore set in line, the engine is a *tandem compound*; but if, for example, the cylinders are mounted side by side and each is connected to opposite ends of a winding-drum shaft then the engine is a *cross-compound*.

Reciprocating air *compressors* make use of the advantages of compounding, and air is usually compressed in two stages, 'exhaust' from the low-pressure cylinder passing to the high-pressure inlet for further compression.

Compressor - a machine for pressurising air which can then be transmitted and used as a power source for driving other machinery, especially underground. Compressors can be either the *rotary* or *turbo* type, where a vaned shaft rotating at high speed draws air in through a valve and forces it out through another under pressure, or the more common *reciprocating piston* type, which acts in the opposite way to a steam-engine by drawing air in to a cylinder, compressing it with a piston, and exhausting it under pressure. With both types, air can be compressed in stages to give a greater force. Compressed air is stored in a sealed tank or *air receiver* until it is required for use.

Creeper - a fixed device for moving *trams*. Lugs on a motor-driven endless chain or rope set between the rails engage with the tram and can haul it, usually up an incline, to where it is required. Trams usually leave the shaft top down a gentle gradient to the screens or washery conveyor, then complete a circuit incorporating one or more creepers to return them to the cage decking level.

Detaching hook - a special hook attaching the cage to the winding-rope. In the event of the winding engine over-running, the hook is drawn into the *overwind*

catch, mounted in the *headframe*, where it releases the cage. The catch holds the cage firmly to prevent it falling down the shaft.

Downcast shaft - see *Shaft*.

Dram - see *Tram*.

Drift - a sloping tunnel connecting the surface with underground workings; coal is carried up through the drift by railway or conveyor belt. A *fan drift* is a short air passage between the *fan* and the *upcast shaft*.

Évasée - a tapering chimney through which exhaust air from the main *fan* is directed to the atmosphere. It was found that if the chimney cross-section expanded gradually towards the outlet, the air speed and pressure were reduced. This increased the fan's effectiveness by diminishing the back pressure on it.

Fan - A colliery usually has several kinds of fan. The *main fan* is set at the end of a short tunnel or *fan drift* connected to the *upcast shaft*, and is responsible for the continuous ventilation of the mine. In the event of a breakdown or maintenance requirements a *standby fan* is available. When a mine has been extended beyond the capability of the main fan to ventilate it properly, *booster fans* are used to assist, and can be installed underground as well as at the surface. An *auxiliary fan* is installed temporarily where a new *heading* is being driven and is not yet linked to the main ventilation system.

Firedamp - methane, an inflammable gas released during mining operations; it is often extracted for use as a fuel within the colliery.

Free-steered vehicle - see under *Haulage*.

Gate road - an underground *roadway* between a main or trunk roadway and the working coalface. *Main* and *tail* gate roads serve each end of a *longwall* face, and are used for access, ventilation, transporting coal and materials, and the various electrical, hydraulic and air services necessary for mining operations.

Gob - the space left after removal of coal; the roof is supported by packing stones into the space or left to fall in a controlled manner. See also *Packs*.

Haulage - the method of underground transport of men, materials and coal. Motive power can be moveable - manual or horse in earlier times, slowly replaced by battery, electric or diesel locomotives; or fixed - by steam, compressed air, electric or hydraulic *capstan engine* driving a rope or chain winch. Tyred vehicles known as *free-steered vehicles* have been introduced from the U.S.A., and belt conveyors have been used for manriding and transporting coal.

Fixed-winch systems can be *direct haulage*, where the free end of the rope is attached to the *trams* and they are pulled towards the winch; *main and tail*, similar to direct, but an additional rope is attached to the rear of the trams, run round a pulley mounted at the start of the haulage and back to a secondary drum on the winch, so that loaded trams are pulled towards the winch by the main rope and the tail rope can haul back empty trams when the engine is reversed; or *endless rope*, where a continuous moving rope runs between two pulleys, one at each end of the haulage, and trams are attached and detached as required. Similar haulage systems were sometimes used on the surface. A variant of the fixed system uses an overhead monorail from which materials to be moved are suspended; an advantage of this system is that the *roadway* floor can be kept clear of obstructions.

Advertising the versatility and financial benefits of electric engines. ('The Colliery Guardian', 26 Jan.1900)

Headframe - a structure at the top of a *shaft* on which the winding-pulleys or sheaves are mounted. Early headframes were small timber or cast-iron frames which were developed into substantial steel constructions almost universal in the twentieth century. Many post-nationalization headframes were built of reinforced concrete. The term *headgear* includes both the frame and winding-pulleys.

Heading - the blind end of a *roadway* which is being cut; nowadays this is done by a *roadheader*.

Heapstead - a large covered area around the pit top or *bank* enclosing the *tram* railway circuit, which includes equipment for removing trams from the *cages*, discharging the coal, usually in a rotary *tippler*, and returning empties to the *shaft* top.

Horizon mining - a method of working a steeply inclined coal seam by driving horizontal *roadways* at different levels from a *shaft* to intersect with and gain access to the seam.

Horse-power - British unit of power; 1 horse-power (h.p.) = 745.7 watts.

Inbye - towards the coalface.

Intake airway - see *Airway*.

Koepe winder - a winding system, named after its inventor, where ropes and *cages* formed a continuous loop suspended over a large driving-pulley mounted in the *headframe*. Also known as a *friction winder*, it relied upon sufficient grip between the rope and the timber-lined tread of the pulley. Apart from the weight of coal being raised, the whole system was in balance and required less power input than a conventional drum winder.

Level or **adit** - a tunnel driven horizontally or on a slight gradient to connect underground workings with the surface. A level can be used for draining water from a mine (when it is generally known as a *drainage adit*) or for transport of coal or both. Some were laid with rails for *trams* whereas others were sufficiently large (and wet) to be used as underground canals.

Longwall - a mining method where coal is cut from a long face or wall running between two parallel *gate roads*.

Mine car - a more sophisticated, larger and stronger form of *tram*, suitable for locomotive powered high-speed coal transportation.

Outbye - away from the coalface.

Overwind catch - see *Detaching hook*.

Packs - stone-built side walls of underground *roadways* which support the roof and prevent ventilation air leaking between the intake and return *airways*. See also *Gob*.

Panel - an area of coal to be removed.

Pillar and stall - a mining method where the seam is excavated leaving pillars of coal to support the roof; these were traditionally left. As adapted for machine cutting, two sets of parallel tunnels at a right-angle are cut through the coal seam; the resultant pillars left supporting the roof can be removed on retreating from the area. Originally hewn by hand-pick, later assisted by explosives, the coal nowadays is cut by continuous mining machines and loaded directly to conveyor belts or trams. Opencast mining removes earlier pillars.

Picking belt - a moving conveyor where large stones or other debris are picked from the coal manually. Although electromagnets and stone crushers now deal with most major impurities in the raw coal; wood, plastic and non-ferrous metal are still removed manually in some collieries.

Plough - a coal-cutting machine used in *longwall* mining which planes a narrow cut from the working face as it is hauled along the *armoured flexible conveyor*, allowing coal to fall onto the conveyor. It was developed in Germany in the 1940s, and became popular in south Wales.

Regulator or **air door** - a door across a return *airway* with an opening and a sliding panel. By varying the effective size of the opening, the quantity of ventilation air available to different areas of a mine can be controlled.

Return airway - see Airway.

Roadway - a tunnel driven to the coalface for access, transport and carrying services and ventilation air. A *trunk* or *main* roadway is the principal passage in a mine.

Roadheader - a powerful self-propelled machine with a moveable cutting head, capable of driving a tunnel continuously through coal or rock and loading out the spoil for removal.

Rock-bolting or **roof-bolting** - method of stabilising a roof by drilling deep holes and fixing bolts, to which are attached wire mesh panels. Where a coal seam roof is unstable, long wooden or plastic bolts can be bonded into place to give temporary support; when the coal is cut such bolts cause no damage to the cutting machinery. Support of *roadways* is normally by steel arches or props.

Screens - an arrangement of fixed or vibrating bars or perforated steel sheets for grading coal by size.

Self-advancing roof supports - used in fully-mechanized *longwall* mining, the system consists of a bank of cantilever or shield canopies carried on hydraulic props which are attached to the *armoured flexible conveyor* by hydraulic rams. The conveyor is pushed across to the face after the cutter has passed, the roof supports release in turn, follow the conveyor and automatically reset.

Shaft - since legislation in 1867, each mine must have at least two passages, shafts, *drifts* or *levels*, connecting the underground workings with the surface to allow escape in the event of one passage becoming impassable, and to enable sufficient air to enter and leave the mine. In deep mines two vertical shafts are sunk; fresh air passes into the mine through the *downcast shaft* and circulates around the working areas, stale air from the mine is then removed through the *upcast shaft*.

In shafts deeper than 45m, *shaft guides* are required by regulation to control the conveyance and may be either tensioned wire ropes or rigid sections of steel or timber.

Shearer - the Anderton shearer loader, a coal-cutting and loading machine introduced for *longwall* mining in the early 1950s. It runs along the *armoured flexible conveyor*, and the cutters arranged round a rotating drum remove coal which falls onto the conveyor.

Skip - a container in which coal is carried up the *shaft*.

Stoppings - airtight walls built to seal off disused underground working areas.

Tippler - a device for emptying *trams*; usually a rotary tippler into which a tram is pushed, clamped in a cradle which then turns sideways through a full circle, emptying the tram's contents into a bunker or railway wagon below.

Tram or **tub** - a small, wheeled truck running on rails and used for carrying coal or materials. *Dram* is the more common term in south Wales.

Trepanner - a cutting machine for *longwall* mining, originally running on the floor but later mounted on the *armoured flexible conveyor*. The rotating head has cutters set around the periphery and is driven into the seam along the coalface. As with the *shearer*, coal is loaded directly onto the conveyor. It was introduced in the 1950s by the Anderson Boyes Company.

Tub - see *Tram*.

Upcast shaft - see *Shaft*.

Washery - see *Coal-preparation plant*.

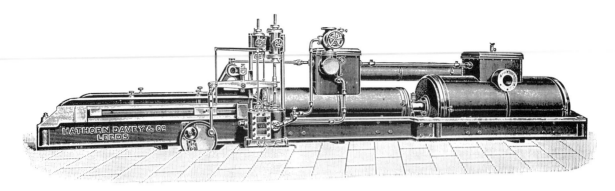

Illustration of a horizontal compound differential pumping engine. (C.M.Percy, 'The Mechanical Equipment of Collieries'.)

Derelict Hathorn Davey tandem compound pumping engine in the basement of the winding-house at Marine Colliery.

Surviving Colliery Machinery

Surviving colliery machinery in Wales accessible to the public:

Winding-engines:

- The only intact water-balance in Wales, from the Rhymney Valley, has been re-erected at Big Pit, Blaenavon.

- The first steam-winder in the Rhondda, from Newbridge Colliery, Pontypridd, stands in front of the former School of Mines, now part of the University of Glamorgan, Treforest. The beam-engine, intact except for its winding-drum, was built by the Varteg Ironworks in 1845.

- At Hetty Shaft, near the Rhondda Heritage Park, Pontypridd, the engine house contains a two-cylinder simple horizontal winder of 1875, 36in. (0.91m.) bore x 72in. (1.83m.) stroke, by Barker & Cope of Kidsgrove, extensively rebuilt in about 1910 following accident damage but containing many original parts. Originally installed with a flat-rope drum, it was converted to take round rope during rebuilding. The engine is currently mothballed and not on public view at the moment.

- A two-cylinder simple steam winder manufactured in about 1890, 42in. (1.07m.) bore x 72in. (1.83m.) stroke, maker unknown but thought to be Henry Fowler of Leeds, is at the Rhondda Heritage Park (formerly Lewis Merthyr Colliery) and drives a bi-cylindro-conical drum. The other winder on site was originally steam powered but electrified in the mid-1950s and also retains its original drum.

- At Elliot Colliery, Tredegar, is the last survivor of the most sophisticated type of winder, a four-cylinder tandem compound of 1891 by Thornewill & Warham, Burton-on-Trent. Originally built as a two-cylinder simple, some 20 years later it was converted to a compound with the addition of high pressure cylinders, 28in. (0.71m.) bore x 72in. (1.83m.) stroke. After rebuilding, the low-pressure exhaust drove a turbine for generating electricity, then passed through a condenser and returned to the boilers. There is a 25ft. (7.6m.) drum of a type unique in Wales: a 'diabolo' drum, which is a bi-cylindro-conical type but with the smaller diameter in the centre. Rhymney Borough Council are currently restoring the engine and house.

- A small two-cylinder simple winding-engine originally from Morlais Colliery, Llangennech, and built by Andrew Barclay of Kilmarnock in about 1905 can be seen at Kidwelly Industrial Museum.

- The two-cylinder simple winding-engine by Worsley Menses of Wigan, 1924, has been removed from Point of Ayr Colliery and is due for re-erection at the Bersham Heritage Centre.

- A two-cylinder winder, 36in. (0.91m.) bore x 60in. (1.52m.) stroke, built by Worsley Mesnes of Wigan in 1927, is now electrically driven for demonstration purposes at the Cefn Coed Colliery Museum, near Neath.

- The only working small electric winder in south Wales, by Uskside of Newport, was installed in 1953 at Big Pit, Blaenavon.

Boiler Installation:

- The only surviving colliery boiler house installation in Wales, complete with Lancashire boilers and chimney, is preserved at Cefn Coed Colliery Museum, near Neath.

Fan Engine:

- A four-cylinder triple expansion fan engine of 1908 from Crumlin Navigation Colliery, the only surviving example in Wales of a large fan engine, formerly used to drive a Walker fan, is in the Welsh Industrial and Maritime Museum, Cardiff.

Pumping Engine:

- A Hathorn Davey horizontal tandem compound pumping-engine dating from the 1890s stands by the entrance to the former Marine Colliery, near Cwm in Ebbw Vale. The cylinders are 36in. (0.91m.) and 68in. (1.73m.) bore, with a stroke of 120in. (3.05m.).

Haulage Engines:

- A rare early example of a south Wales ironworks product, a two-cylinder simple vertical engine, for flat rope endless haulage, and built by the Ebbw Vale Iron Company *ca.*1864, is on view at the South Wales Miners Museum, Afan Argoed Country Park.

- One of the few south Wales engines surviving from Llewellyn & Cubitt, Tonpentre is a single cylinder haulage engine of 1874 from Parc Colliery, Treorci. Used for hauling supplies up old coal tips to the upcast shaft, it is in the Welsh Industrial and Maritime Museum, Cardiff.

- A collection of four electrically driven underground haulages, along with several steam and compressed-air haulage engines in varying stages of restoration, can be seen at Big Pit, Blaenavon.

- A single-cylinder capstan from Llewellyn & Cubitt, Tonpentre, and a two-cylinder cross-compound drift haulage engine from Morlais Colliery, Llangennech, and built by Andrew Barclay of Kilmarnock, are at Cefn Coed Colliery Museum, near Neath.

- There is a typical two-cylinder compressed-air haulage by John Mills of Llanidloes (who were major manufacturers of small haulages for south Wales) at the South Wales Miners Museum, Afan Argoed Country Park. Also at the museum is a unique three-cylinder vertical engine with open-topped cylinders built in Bridgend. Both engines are in working order and operated occasionally on compressed air.

Gazetteer of Protected Colliery Sites

This appendix gives details of buildings and sites which are currently afforded statutory protection by listing or scheduling following a thematic survey of coalmining remains by **Cadw: Welsh Historic Monuments.** It is complete as of September 1994, though further colliery sites may be added to the statutory lists or schedule in future. The appendix encompasses sites and buildings of coal production and processing throughout Wales. Listed or scheduled features associated with the transportation or marketing of coal outside the colliery or with the social history of mining communities are not included.

   Scheduled ancient monuments are indicated in this appendix by the letter (**S**) in brackets after site names, and buildings of special architectural or historic interest by the letter (**L**). Further information about scheduled ancient monuments may be obtained from Cadw: **Welsh Historic Monuments, Brunel House, 2 Fitzalan Road, Cardiff, CF2 1UY.** Further information about listed buildings can be obtained from the relevant local planning authority. Information about all these sites is held by the **National Monuments Record, Royal Commission on the Ancient and Historical Monuments of Wales, Plas Crug, Aberystwyth, Dyfed, SY23 1NJ.**

Most of the sites on this list are in private ownership.

Listing or scheduling does not provide any right of access to the public.

Abersychan (Lower Navigation Colliery)   SO 2537 0396
engine house, Abersychan (**L**)
A brick engine house of *ca.*1900 for a winding engine, generator and fan engine, with a rare surviving Waddle fan base adjoining.

Abersychan (Lower Navigation Colliery) engine house is now in light industrial use.

Bryngwyn engine house had a line of pump-rods running from an arch in the rusticated basement into a nearby mine tunnel.

Bersham Colliery, Wrexham (**L**) and (**S**)   SJ 3143 4820

A colliery started in 1864, and closed in 1986. The lattice girder headframe installed in 1935 is scheduled, and the 1930s winding engine house with its electric winding engine installed in 1962 and the baths building of 1952 are listed. The engine house and headframe are under restoration. Associated buildings and a tip are nearby.

Bettisfield Colliery, Bagillt (**L**)   SJ 2153 7594

A large brick horizontal winding engine house, a stone heapstead and a lamproom, all dating from the 1880s.

Bonville's Court Colliery, Saundersfoot (**L**)   SN 1249 0528

A power house, weighbridge house and heapstead from a leading Pembrokeshire colliery which operated from 1842 to 1930.

British pumping engine house, Abersychan (**S**)   SO 2584 0364

A well preserved beam pumping engine house of 1845 which served coal workings on the site of the British Ironworks.

Bryngwyn engine house, Bedwas (**S**)   ST 1620 8928

A tall ruined engine house of *ca*.1868, thought to have housed an inverted single action 'Bull' engine used for pumping and probably haulage in the adjacent drifts until 1903.

Cefn Coed Colliery, Crynant (**L**)   SN 7852 0322

An anthracite colliery sunk in 1926-27 and closed in 1968, though several structures continued in use by Blaenant Colliery. There are two lattice girder headframes, a row of Lancashire boilers, an engine house with original steam winders and compressors, a pumphouse and a tall chimney. A museum was established on the site in 1978.

Clyne Valley shaft mounds, Swansea (**S**)   SS 6100 9180

Large area of earthworks from bell pits and deeper shafts developed from the seventeenth to nineteenth centuries, and especially after the opening of the Oystermouth Railway in the valley in 1804. Situated in the Clyne Valley County Park.

Clyne Wood coal level, Swansea (**S**)   SS 6126 9123

An early nineteenth-century rock cut and stone lined adit entrance of *ca*.1840 adjacent to the Clyne Wood canal built *ca*.1800. Situated in Clyne Valley Country Park.

Clyne Wood winding engine, Swansea (**S**)   SS 6032 9202

A small twin-cylindered horizontal winding engine to a design by J. Wild and Co., of Oldham dated 1891, probably installed *ca*.1912. It is situated next to stone engine beds on top of coal tips in the Clyne Valley Country Park.

Crumlin Navigation Colliery, Crumlin (**L**)   ST 2107 9890

A show pit of unusual architectural quality, built by Partridge, Jones & Co. in 1907-11. It closed in 1967. There are two winding engine houses, a pumping house, stores and workshops, a magnificent chimney, offices, a fan house, heapstead, powder store and baths.

Cwmbyrgwm Colliery, Abersychan (**S**)　　　　SO 2510 0330

Mining began here before 1820 and expanded with the development of the British Ironworks in 1827. There is a rich mining landscape around the remains of a scheduled water-balance headgear, including a brick chimney of *ca.*1880, waste tips, several oval shafts, two water power dams and tramroad routes.

Cwm Coke Works wooden cooling towers,　　　　ST 0658 8610
Llantwit Fardre (**L**)

Cwm Colliery operated from 1909 to 1986, and a coke works was established on the site by the National Coal Board in 1957. Two cooling towers built entirely of timber following the traditional pattern are listed, and the coke works is still in operation.

Cwmdu airshaft and fan, Merthyr Tydfil (**S**)　　　　SO 0315 0519

A rare surviving example of small ventilation fan typical of a turn of the century small mine, with a narrow airshaft. Some associated pithead buildings are nearby.

Crumlin Navigation Colliery (1907-11) with its polychrome brickwork and formal layout is of unusual architectural quality.

Cwmbyrgwm Colliery has left a rich mining landscape; visible here is an oval shaft top and a chimney of ca.1880.

Cwm Pelenna ventilation furnace, Tonmawr (**S**)   SS 8171 9720
A short stone chimney and hillside flue for a furnace ventilation system to a level of the 1830s.

Cwm ventilation furnace, Ebbw Vale (**L**)   SO 1879 0375
A squat circular brick ventilation chimney and shaft, built in the 1840s or 1850s and disused by 1876; the only example of this typical mid nineteenth-century form known to survive in Wales.

Cyfarthfa canal level, Merthyr Tydfil (**S**)   SO 0428 0534 and 0423 0546

The entrance to a boat-operated level of the late eighteenth or early nineteenth centuries, and a section of the Cyfarthfa Canal, a two mile (3.2km.) long tub boat canal built in the 1770s and disused by 1840.

Elliot Colliery engine house, New Tredegar (**S**)   SO 1474 0272

A stone built winding engine house for a colliery which operated from 1883 to 1967. The exceptionally large horizontal engine contained is as built in 1891 and modified to compound working in *ca.*1911.

Genwen engine house, Llanelli (**S**)   SS 5457 9957

A rare surviving Boulton and Watt steam engine house of 1806, built on the site of an earlier Newcomen engine house. The structure was enlarged in 1837 and used until 1908. A level entrance of the 1830s is just to the west.

Glynea Colliery, Llanelli (**S**)   SS 5479 9914

Ruins showing clearly the layout of a colliery sunk *ca.*1860, including a beam engine house, horizontal winding house, fan house and heapstead. A tip and ancillary building are nearby.

Glyn Pits, Pontypool (**S**)   ST 2656 9983

Two steam engines in stone engine houses, now in a derelict condition: one a Neath Abbey beam engine of 1845 for winding and pumping, and the other a vertical winding engine installed in the 1850s, possibly second-hand. A small fan and a reservoir with a stone dam nearby are also scheduled.

Grove Colliery engine house, Stepaside (**S**)   SN 1393 0711

A fine stone beam engine house of *ca.*1847, built in association with the nearby Stepaside Ironworks. The tramroad to the ironworks, and the ironworks themselves, are also scheduled.

Gwernllwynchwith engine house, Swansea (**S**)   SS 6975 9796

Ruined structure of possibly the earliest surviving rotary engine house in Britain, believed to have been built *ca.*1772-82 to house a winding engine.

Henllys Vale Colliery, Cwmllynfell (**L**)   SN 7621 1372

A tall boilerhouse chimney and associated limekilns which formed part of an anthracite drift which operated from 1898 to 1918. The kilns were used with local coal from the 1880s.

Hetty Pit, Pontypridd (**L** and **S**)   ST 0546 9090

A complete Barker and Cope steam winding engine of 1875 in its original engine house, with a steel joist headframe, fan house, heapstead and steam winch.

Kilgetty Colliery, Kilgetty (**L**)   SN 1383 0777

An anthracite colliery of the early nineteenth century, re-developed in the 1930s, with a weighbridge house, ventilation drift and inter-war winding engine house. Another winding engine house has been converted nearby.

Lefel Fawr, Ystradgynlais (**L** and **S**)   SN 8153 1243

A rock cut level established *ca.*1796, with a stone bridge of *ca.*1824 over the River Tawe, and a manager's house and office of the early nineteenth century.

Elliot Colliery engine house still contains an exceptionally large winding engine of 1891; made into a compound in ca.1911.

Lewis Merthyr Colliery, Trehafod (**L**)   ST 0399 9114

An exceptionally complete complex established by W.T. Lewis (Lord Merthyr) in the mid 1870s and closed in 1983. The buildings include the two oldest headframes remaining in Wales, complete pitheads, a lamproom, two fan houses, two winding engine houses with one electric and one steam winder, and a chimney. Now the Rhondda Heritage Park.

Llantrisant (or Ynysmaerdy) Colliery,   ST 0326 8404
Llantrisant (**L**)

An outstanding Powell Duffryn complex built after World War I and closed in 1942, including a large engine hall, assembly shops, a winding engine-house, stores, revetment wall, concrete reservoir and explosives store.

Llay Hall Colliery, Wrexham (**L**)   SJ 3156 5511

A winding and fan house, workshops, chimney and former washery building, from a colliery which operated from 1877 to 1948. Some ancillary buildings also survive.

Llwynypia Engine House, Llwynypia (**L**)   SS 9936 9328

A large brick power house of the Glamorgan Colliery at Llwynypia, built in 1905. In November 1910 it was at the centre of the Tonypandy Riots, when strikers stormed the building during the Cambrian Collieries dispute.

Marine pumping engine, Ebbw Vale (**S**)   SO 1883 0425

A Hathorn Davey steam pumping engine of 1893, relocated to near the roadside following removal from a chamber beneath a winding engine house at the former Marine Colliery.

Nant Mill Wood shaft mounds, Wrexham (**S**)   SJ 2810 5055

An area of earthworks from bell pits or shallow shaft working in the eighteenth and nineteenth centuries.

Newbridge beam engine, Pontypridd (**S**)   ST 0826 8852

A steam winding engine, believed to have been the first in the Rhondda area, built by Varteg Ironworks in *ca.*1845 and operating at Newbridge Colliery until 1919. It was re-erected in the grounds of Treforest School of Mines, now the University of Glamorgan, in 1920.

Ogilvie powder store, Bargoed (**L**)   SO 1190 0323

A typical early twentieth century vaulted explosives store from the former Ogilvie Colliery, which operated from World War I to 1975. The building is within the Darran Valley Country Park.

Penallta Colliery, Gelligaer (**L**)   ST 1399 9585

A pioneering complex of the Powell Duffryn combine, built in 1906 and closed in 1992. The huge common engine hall was one of the earliest in Britain, and the surface buildings were efficiently laid out around two steel joist headframes. The lamproom, stores, workshops and pit-top office are in matching style. The baths of 1938 are one of the finest by the Miners Welfare Committee.

Penprys Pit, Llanelli (**S**)   SN 5400 0181

A winding engine house built *ca.*1890 for an early to mid nineteenth-century whim engine. The engine beds, drum beds and shaft top are intact.

Penrhos engine house, Brymbo (**S**)   SJ 2856 5322

A beam engine house, probably housing a Hornblower engine, built for a colliery established by John Wilkinson *ca.*1794.

Plas Power Colliery, Wrexham (**L**)   SJ 2991 5193

Two ruined winding houses, a power house, heapstead and workshops from one of the larger north Wales collieries, established in 1875 and closed in 1938. There are also some ancillary buildings and a large tip.

Rhode Wood shaft mounds, Saundersfoot (**S**)   SN 0381 0423

An area of primitive anthracite workings from between the eighteenth century and the 1860s.

St David's Colliery, Llanelli (**S**)   SN 5395 0135

A group of pit top structures built by the Llangennech Coal Company in 1825, at what became for some time the deepest mine in Wales at 660 feet. The remains include a stone beam engine house, heapstead, ruins of ancillary buildings, and an unusual steam haulage house for an incline from Penprys Colliery built *ca.*1889.

Scott's Pit, Swansea (**S**)   SS 6972 9830

A Cornish pumping engine house built 1817-19 and worked until 1842, then re-used for pumping from 1872. The chimney, boiler bases, shaft and tips have been excavated and are in a public park.

The Plas Power Colliery buildings are one of the main survivals of the north-east Wales collieries.

Tower Colliery, Hirwaun (**L**)   SN 9264 0417

The site of nineteenth-century workings, re-developed in the 1930s and 1950s, and privatised in 1994. The small Powell Duffryn engine hall of *ca.*1941 and the lattice girder headframe are listed.

Tredegar coal block, Tredegar (**L**)   SO 1416 0853

Probably the largest block of coal ever cut. It weighed 15 tons and came from the nearby Yard Level for the Great Exhibition in 1851, though transporting it there proved too difficult. A two ton block cut for the 1951 Festival of Britain is alongside. Both are under a cover building with other mining artefacts in Bedwellty Park.

Trehafod ventilation furnace, Trehafod (**S**)   ST 0428 9123

A nineteenth-century colliery ventilation furnace with a short chimney and ventilation drift.

Underhill Wood coal workings, Jeffreyston (**S**)   SN 0895 0673

A complex of earthworks typical of the early anthracite industry in Pembrokeshire and documented as having operated from the sixteenth to nineteenth centuries. It includes opencasts, bell pits and subsidence features.

Waun-y-coed Colliery, Pontardawe (**S**)   SN 7384 0495

A drift entrance with engine house base, chimney and tippling wall, adjacent to a scheduled tramroad incline and, across the River Tawe, a branch canal basin from the Swansea Canal, formerly linked to the colliery by a timber bridge.

The impressive winding-house at Wynnstay Colliery (1856) near Ruabon housed a double, inverted, vertical steam-powered winding-engine. The internal support walls partition the engine-house between the tall central, and smaller flanking openings. These iron-reinforced cross-walls supported the drum at a high level with flat wire ropes exiting through the smaller dormer window in the roof and through the high central opening in the wall below. Wooden headframes were supported both from the small openings flanking the upper part of the high central opening and originally from the similar blocked holes flanking the lower part of the opening. (redrawn from survey by J.A.Felton; Welsh School of Architecture Collection)

Wynnstay Colliery, Ruabon (**S**)   SJ 2933 4332
A vertical winding engine house of *ca.*1856 and a Walker fan house of 1902. Ancillary buildings from the colliery, which operated from 1856 to 1927, are nearby.

Ynysgedwyn Colliery fan house, Ystradgynlais (**S**)   SN 8016 1113
The ruined remains of a masonry chamber, engine bed and brick évasée for a Guibal fan house of *ca.*1880.

Ynys Pit and leat, Swansea (**S**)   SS 6142 9190
A water powered colliery site operated from the 1840s until before 1877, together with a well-preserved length of Sir John Morris's water power leat built *ca.*1800. The site is within the Clyne Valley Country Park.

Index

(Illustrations are indicated by numbers in **bold** type)

Royal Commission publications

Publications produced by the Royal Commission and available from:

Alan Sutton Publishing, Phoenix Mill, Far Thrupp, Stroud, Gloucs, GL5 2BU.

The Archaeology of the Montgomeryshire Canal: A Guide and Study in Waterways Archaeology.
By Stephen Hughes   (4th edition, 2nd impression)

A Guide to the Industrial archaeology of the Swansea Region.
By Stephen Hughes and Paul Reynolds   (2nd edition)

The Archaeology of an Early Railway System: The Brecon Forest Tramroads.
By Stephen Hughes

Lighthouses of Wales: Their Architecture and Archaeology.
By Douglas B. Hague   (edited by Stephen Hughes)

Wales from the Air: Patterns of Past and Present.
By Chris Musson

Other Royal Commission publications are :

Glamorgan Inventory :

Volume III Part 1a - **The Early Castles (from the Norman Conquest to 1217).**
Volume III Part II - **Medieval Non-defensive Secular Monuments.**
Volume IV Part I - **The Greater Houses.**
Volume IV Part II - **Farmhouses and Cottages.**

Brecknock Inventory :

Volume I Part II - **Hill-forts and Roman Remains.**

Houses of the Welsh Countryside: A Study in Historical Geography.
By Peter Smith   (2nd edition)

The visual material used in these publications is a selection from the archive of the National Monuments Record of Wales, which is open to the public between 9.30am and 4.00pm - Monday to Friday, at the address below :

Royal Commission on the Ancient and Historical Monuments of Wales, Plas Crug, Aberystwyth, Dyfed, SY23 1NJ.